THE CHARLTON
STANDARD CATALOGUE OF

LILLIPUT LANE COTTAGES

THIRD EDITION

BY
ANNETTE AND TOM POWER

W.K. CROSS
PUBLISHER

TORONTO, ONTARIO • PALM HARBOR, FLORIDA

COPYRIGHT AND TRADEMARK NOTICE

ENESCO EUROPEAN GIFTWARE GROUP, LTD.

OTHER COPYRIGHTS

DISCLAIMERS

While every care has been taken to ensure accuracy in the compilation of the data in this catalogue, the publisher cannot accept responsibility for typographical errors and omissions.

Printed in Canada

EDITORIAL

Editor	Jean Dale
Editorial Assistant	Cindy Raycroft
Graphic Technician	Davina Rowan

ACKNOWLEDGEMENTS

The Charlton Press and the author wish to thank those who have helped with the third edition of The Charlton Standard Catalogue of Lilliput Lane Cottages.

CONTRIBUTORS TO THE THIRD EDITION

Ray Day, Ray Day Studio, New Albany; Claire Golata, Enesco Corp. Itasca; Jane Hill, Lynne Hunter and Patricia Potts, European Giftware Group Limited; Gerhild Somann of N.C. Cameron & Sons Limited, Toronto.

A SPECIAL NOTE TO COLLECTORS

The Charlton Press has an ongoing commitment to excellence and completeness in the production of all its reference works. We will consider editorial additions or corrections regarding colourways, varieties, or dating of patterns. Your help in providing new or previously unobtainable data on any aspect of Lilliput Lane collecting will be considered for inclusion in subsequent editions. Those providing information will be acknowledged in the contributor's section of this catalogue.

Please send your contributions together with your name, address and phone number to our editorial offices in Toronto.

Canadian Cataloguing In Publication Data

Power, Annette
The Charlton standard catalogue of Lilliput Lane cottages
3rd ed.
First ed. published under title: The collector's handbook of Lilliput Lane cottages; 2nd ed. published under title: The Charlton standard catalogue of Lilliput Lane.
ISSN 1492-4102
ISBN 0-88968-222-4

1. Lilliput Lane Limited - Catalogues. 2. Pottery, English - Catalogs.
3. Miniature pottery - England - Catalogs. I. Power, Tom. II. Title.

NK4210.L48P68 2000 738.8'2 C00-930973-X

Editorial Office
2040 Yonge Street, Suite 208, Toronto, Ontario. M4S 1Z9
Telephone: (416) 488-1418 Fax: (416) 488-4656
Telephone: (800) 442-6042 Fax: (800) 442-1542
www.charltonpress.com; e-mail: chpress@charltonpress.com

HOW TO USE THIS CATALOGUE

THE LISTINGS

This book has been designed to serve two specific purposes. First, to furnish the Lilliput Lane enthusiast with accurate listings containing vital information and photographs to aid in the building of a rewarding collection. Secondly, this publication provides Lilliput Lane collectors and dealers with current market prices for the complete line of Lilliput Lane cottages.

Within the individual listings, the pieces are listed in alphabetical order. After the item's name comes **Size**, **Backstamp**, the date of **Introduction** and withdrawal, and **Varieties** (if applicable). The **Series** to which the piece belongs is listed next. Lastly, the suggested retail price is given in Canadian, American and British funds.

VARIETY CLASSIFICATIONS

Collectors will note the following distinction concerning styles, versions and variations:

STYLES: When two or more cottages have the same name but different physical modelling characteristics, they are listed as **Style One, Style Two** and so on after their names.

VERSIONS: Versions are modifications in a major style element.

VARIATIONS: Variations are modifications in a minor style element. A change in colour is a variation.

A WORD ON PRICING

In addition to providing accurate information, this catalogue gives readers the most up-to-date retail prices for Lilliput Lane cottages in Canadian, American and British currencies.

To accomplish this, The Charlton Press continues to access an international pricing panel of Lilliput Lane experts that submits prices based on both dealer and collector retail-price activity, as well as current auction results. These market prices are carefully averaged to reflect accurate valuations in each of these three markets.

Please be aware that all prices given in a particular currency are for cottages within that particular country. The prices published herein have not been calculated using exchange rates exclusively. They have been determined solely by supply and demand within the country in question.

A necessary word of caution. No pricing catalogue can be, or should be, a fixed price list. This catalogue, therefore, should be considered as a pricing guide only — showing the most current retail prices based on market demand within a particular region for the various items.

Current cottages, however, are priced differently in this catalogue. Such pieces are priced according to the manufacturers suggested retail price in each of the three market regions. It should be noted that it is likely dealer discounting from these prices will occur.

One exception, however, occurs in the case of current models or recent limited editions issued in only one of the three markets. Since such items were priced by Lillput Lane only in the country in which they were to be sold, prices for other markets are not shown.

The prices published herein are for pieces in mint condition. Collectors are cautioned that a repaired or restored piece may be worth as little as 25 per cent of the value of the same piece in mint condition. The collector interested strictly in investment potential will avoid damaged figurines.

THE INTERNET AND PRICING

The Internet is changing the way business is being done in the collectable marketplace. Linking millions of collectors around the world through chat rooms, antique and collector malls, Internet auctions and producer web sites, e-commerce has become big business.

Some of the effects caused by the Internet and e-commerce on the collectable business are as follows:

1. Collectors deal directly with other collectors, changing the dynamics of the traditional customer/dealer relationship.
2. Information concerning new issues, finds and varieties is readily available, twenty-four hours a day. Collectors' wants are made known instantly to a wide spectrum of dealers and collectors.
3. Prices:

   (a) Price differentials will disappear between global market areas as collectors and the delivery services team up to stretch the purchasing power of the collectable dollar/pound.

   (b) Prices of common to scarce items will adjust downward to compensate for the temporary expansion of merchandise supply. Conversely, prices of rare and extremely rare items will increase, a result of additional exposure to demand.

   (c) After a time even the prices of the common items will rise due to the growing worldwide demand for collectables.
4. Internet auction sites listing millions of items for sale on a daily basis continue to grow as more and more collectors discover the viability of using this method to buy and sell merchandise.
5. Traditional marketing strategies (retail stores, direct-mail retailers, collectable shows and fairs, and collectable magazines and papers) face increased pressure in a more competitive environment.

The Internet is user-friendly: no travelling required, twenty-four hour accessibility, no face-to-face contact or other pressure to buy or sell. Without a doubt, the arrival of e-commerce will change the way a collector collects.

TABLE OF CONTENTS

INTRODUCTION

Discovering Lilliput Lane Cottages

One of the best ways to learn about Lilliput Lane past and present is to visit their Collectors Centre at Skirsgill, near Penrith, Cumbria. The lure of the company museum, showroom and studio tour, set in spectacular Lake District scenery, draws collectors from all over the world and they return home even more knowledgeable and enthusiastic about their chosen hobby. The centre is only open to members of the Lilliput Lane Collectors Club and advance booking is required for the studio tour.

Vernacular Architecture

The journey north from London passes through many of the areas celebrated in the Lilliput Lane collection and, if time allows, it is worth a detour to explore the charming Cotswold villages, with cottages built of the local honey-coloured stone, or the black and white timber-framed buildings of the Midlands, aptly described as 'Magpie' style.

Comparing the original buildings with the authentically detailed Lilliput Lane models helps illustrate how the different character of towns and villages have been shaped by the availability of building materials and the development of specialist local crafts, such as thatching or pargeting. Indeed, part of the fun of collecting Lilliput Lane Cottages is having a greater appreciation of vernacular architecture, described by company founder David Tate as "buildings built by the people for the people with the materials that lay around them."

Starting the Company

Travelling north-west into the Lake District, the landscape changes dramatically and hill farms, hewn from local stone, cling to exposed mountain slopes. Thousands of visitors come to this area every year to marvel at the majesty of the scenery and enjoy the climbing and water-sports, and it was here that David Tate decided to base his new cottage company in 1982.

Workshops were found at Skirsgill, near Penrith, in the converted stables of an old mansion house and somewhat basic accommodation was provided at Rose Cottage for David, his wife and two teenage daughters.

The old coach house at Skirsgill, now Gulliver's Pantry

The Collectors Centre

It is hard to imagine the Tate family's spartan existence arriving at the Lilliput Lane workshops today. When the new Collectors Centre was created in 1991, Rose Cottage was converted into a charming little museum and showroom set in a cobbled courtyard, complete with Victorian lamp-posts and a traditional red telephone box, which was rescued from certain destruction. The old coach house for the Skirsgill estate now forms Gulliver's Pantry, which provides welcome refreshments after a tour of the studios. Having started with 800 square feet of workshop space and six staff, the company now dominates the stable block and has expanded to several different sites in Cumbria with some 700 employees.

David Tate

Some collectors may be fortunate enough to meet David Tate during their visit as he is still actively involved in the running of the company, that is when he is not travelling the world with his audio-visual show, presenting the Lilliput Lane cottages to an ever-growing international audience. It was his energy and determination that got the company off the ground and he sustained its growth with a combination of talents, including a strong visual memory and exceptional engineering skills acquired in SRP industry.

His speciality was fibreglass moulding and he developed a new technique for moulding small, intricately detailed cottages in one piece, unlike traditional production methods in the ceramic industry which require sculptures to be assembled from several parts. He was so convinced of the potential of his new cottage models that he sold his house to get started and, despite constant cash-flow problems in the early years, he has succeeded in building up a company which has won the highly-coveted Queen's Award for Export and Achievement and the lion's share of awards at the international collectables shows.

In 1988 he was honoured personally with the MBE and since November 1993 the company has been publicly quoted on the London Stock Exchange - a remarkable catalogue of achievements in just 12 years.

Honeysuckle Cottage Museum

The results of his endeavours can be seen in the Honeysuckle Cottage Museum, which displays a wide range of Lilliput Lane Cottages past and present. The collection began in 1982 with fourteen cottages modelled by David himself. Many were inspired by the vernacular buildings which he had grown to love in the Lake District and his native Yorkshire, for example, Lakeside House and Dale Farm. Rural Hampshire, where he had lived for some years, suggested Honeysuckle Cottage and April Cottage.

A few models from the launch collection are now extremely rare as they were not made for very long, notably Old Mine, which was discontinued after ten months with only 200 pieces produced, and Drapers which was withdrawn at the same time with only 360 pieces made in two different colour treatments.

Technical Developments

Many modelling and colour changes were made to the cottages in the early years as David gradually improved production techniques as well as the body and paint formulations.

The first important development in 1983 was the use of glass-reinforced plastic moulds instead of the traditional plaster type and this enabled much more complex sculptures to be reproduced. Originally a basic Crystacel plaster was used for the body of the cottages, but this was too light weight and brittle and in 1984 he perfected Amorphite, a much harder and stronger material suitable for reproducing more intricate detail.

The paints also needed to be improved as the original colours were liable to fade in bright sunlight. After much experimentation, in 1984 David introduced new earth-based pigments which could be applied in colour washes, enhancing all the different textures of the model, and these were reformulated in 1990 to make them even more transparent and brighter.

Not one to rest on his laurels, David is constantly looking for new ways to improve processes and techniques and his Research and Development department is a hive of activity. For obvious reasons this building is not part of the studio tour nor is the Modelling department where the artists work on the future cottage introductions. However, the Lilliput Lane tour guides explain the nature of all the 'behind the scenes' stages before conducting visitors around the various production processes.

Behind the Scenes

David Tate and his team of artists travel many thousands of miles each year searching out suitable subject matter for the Lilliput Lane collection and they have built up an extensive library of reference books and photographs of vernacular architecture.

Once a specific building has been chosen for reproduction the detailed research begins. It is photographed from every angle and sketches are made on location to capture the unique atmosphere of the property and its surroundings. Back in the studio, the sculptor produces lots of interpretative sketches, emphasizing certain features, before preparing the final working drawing. The scale they work to for the finished sculpture is generally 1/76th of the original building, but that can change.

The sculptors work with a specially formulated wax and they manipulate this warm, malleable material into the basic shape of the building before carving the detail with an assortment of tools.

Dental instruments have proved very useful for achieving the right texture for tiny details, such as bricks or window panes, which are carefully cut into the walls. If the building requires roofing slates or tiles, these are cut from a thin sheet of wax and individually applied - a very time-consuming task.

Many pieces have elaborate gardens which will be 'planted' painstakingly with intricately sculpted bushes and flowers. The artists all study the different flower seasons to ensure their gardens are accurately interpreted.

Generally it takes the sculptors a minimum of two weeks to create a finished wax for the general range, complex prestige or limited edition pieces take much longer.

Touring Production

The wax original is destroyed in the mould-making process so there is no margin for error in the skilled tooling department. First of all a solid block mould is produced in silicone rubber and several resin copies or 'masters' of the original are cast. The master is then coated with a thin layer of plastic, and fibreglass is carefully laid on top of this to form a multi-part case.

After hardening the fibreglass case is removed in sections and the plastic is peeled away from its interior and the outside of the master model. Now, when the case is re-assembled around the master, there is a narrow gap which is injected with silicone rubber to form the finished mould.

Smoothing the base

Finally, a secondary case is made to support the mould during casting and, after thorough testing, all these tools are transferred to the production mould-making department to make lots of silicone rubber working moulds.

Visitors to Lilliput Lane can also watch the casting and de-moulding processes which have been refined over many years. Liquid Amorphite is poured into the silicone rubber moulds, which are supported by back-up moulds whilst they are vibrated at low frequency to remove air bubbles.

As the Amorphite is setting, the base of the cast is levelled. It takes just over half an hour for the Amorphite to set to the required degree and the silicone mould is then removed from the back-up and stripped from the cast. It is not as easy as it looks. De-moulding is a very skilled job and great care must be taken to ensure no tall chimneys or spires are broken off.

De-moulding

Fettling, where unwanted pieces of plaster are removed

Many of the craftsmen and women performing these delicate operations seem very young and David Tate is proud of the fact that the average age in the company is only 25. The various Lilliput Lane studios in Cumbria are major employers of youthful talent and, after intensive training and all the relevant work experience, many school leavers are promoted to responsible positions at an early age.

Before the casts of the cottages are completely hard, the fettlers will remove any unwanted remnants of plaster which remain in deep recesses and the piece is allowed to dry for 24 hours before being dipped in a coloured sealant. The colour of the dip is dependent on the original building materials and visitors can see samples of all the base colours and the different effects they produce. A more prolonged drying period in a de-humidifying chamber follows and the piece is then ready for painting.

For many visitors, this is the most exciting department.The carousels of specially formulated paint create a riot of colour and there is something magical about seeing the cottages come to life with the deft touches of the painter's brush. The intense concentration of the artists creates an intimate atmosphere, which is punctuated only by the gasps of delight from collectors as they see their favourite piece or a future introduction being decorated. Each painter specialises in just a few different models which enables them to work as efficiently as possible. For reference, they have a master copy which has been created after hours of experimentation by the chief colourist. Sometimes more than thirty different effects are tried out in the Colouring department before a final choice is made.

Painting

During the various stages of production, there have been several inspections and sub-standard models are destroyed before they reach the final quality control department. The piece is scrutinised once again and, if satisfactory, is finished with green baize and despatched to Lilliput Lane stockists all over the world.

The Current Range

After an inspirational tour, most collectors want to return to Rose Cottage to buy souvenirs of their visit - a timber-framed and matched life size reproduction of an early Lilliput model,perhaps even a piece they have seen being decorated. The choice is endless as there are representative buildings from every part of the UK - magpie buildings and mills from the Midlands, remote farms and village schools from the North, thatched cottages and pubs from the South-East and seaside cottages from the South-West. Wales is represented by tiny slate-roofed cottages and chapels, Scotland by castles and tenements, and Ireland by crofts and village stores.

The Lilliput Lane studios have also gone further afield for inspiration in response to their growing international audience. In 1986 David Tate and sculptor Tom Raine drove around Northern Europe seeking inspiration for the German collection, which was followed by the French and Dutch collections in 1990 and 1991 respectively. Originally the national collections were only sold in their respective countries.

A log cabin and an adobe village were early, but short lived, introductions to a US series and in 1989 a new direction was taken when Ray Day, one of America's top artists, was commissioned to produce the American Landmarks collection especially for the thousands of Lilliput Lane collectors in the USA.

For collectors conscious of space and budget limitations, a range of miniature cottages, less than 3 inches tall, was added to the range in 1993. The cottages in the Classics collection, now retired, were all inspired by the picturesque village in Blaise Hamlet. Miniature cottages, blanketed in snow (early models have the snow as part of the mould, later ones have "icing sugar" snow applied after painting), have also proved very popular as Christmas gifts and no doubt many new collections will grow from these seasonal 'seeds.'

Building a Collection

Many Lilliput Lane collections grow from chance gifts and, as the delighted recipient gradually succumbs to the infinite charms of the cottages, new purchases follow, sometimes in quick succession! Other collections start from souvenirs purchased at famous British beauty spots and then the fun continues as holidays are spent travelling the country looking for the original buildings which inspired each cottage.

Some collectors become interested in cottages because of their personal associations, for example they have lived in a thatched cottage or been married in a church with the same name or appearance as a Lilliput Lane model. Whatever their starting point, all collectors share the nostalgia for the past which is evoked by all the buildings in the Lilliput range.

It is not unusual for very large collections to be created in comparatively short periods of time as the enthusiasm blossoms. Cabinets and display shelves are built apace and before long it is necessary to convert the spare room or the garage into a showroom! For those aspiring to form a complete collection, it is advisable to keep up with all the introductions to the current range as, once they are discontinued, they can become very elusive. Lilliput Lane regularly retire pieces from the range as David Tate explains, 'We care about collectors and we want to maintain the collectability of our cottages by controlling the numbers rather than just exploiting them.'

Some keen collectors will cross continents in search of retired pieces and stiff competition has led to some meteoric price rises for rare pieces on the secondary market. Auctions of retired pieces have been held at the Lilliput Lane Annual Fair and several specialist dealers are now catering for the demand for discontinued cottages on both sides of the Atlantic. The highest prices are paid for David Tate's first designs with very short production runs. Early versions of cottages with modelling and colour variations also attract a lot of interest. It is hard to believe when the hammer comes down on three- or four-figure prices that the early cottages originally retailed for around £2.50!

Nowadays complex prestige pieces start around £100 in the current price lists, so many collectors need to budget for these special pieces. However, a high price is not a deterrent for spectacular designs as was proved in 1989 with St Peter's Cove, the company's most ambitious and challenging sculpture. The limited edition of 3,000 pieces was sold out within six months and it now changes hands for considerably more than its issue price.

Special commissions with limited distribution, such as the Seven Dwarfs Cottage made for Disney World in 1986 or Mayflower House which was exclusive to the USA in 1989-90 or Out of the Storm (1997), are hard to find today, particularly in the UK. No doubt Counting House Corner, which was produced in a limited edition of 3,093 to mark the company's flotation on the London Stock Exchange, will also be very sought after in the future as the edition was oversubscribed by over 7,000 applications and it was only offered to UK Club members.

The Collectors Club was founded in 1986 and membership grew rapidly from 500 in the first month to over 80,000 members worldwide today. Subscribers receive the informative quarterly magazine Gulliver's World as well as annual joining gifts and exclusive cottage offers. Some of the first Club editions, such as Crendon Manor and Yew Tree Farm, now command high premiums, and even past free gifts fetch surprising prices, in particular Packhorse Bridge and Little Lost Dog.

Skirsgill, the home of the Lilliput Lane Collectors Club

For a brief period the company dabbled in figurative models of clowns and these are now desirable along with the study of Gulliver, the hero of Jonathan Swift's travel tale from which the Lilliput Lane name was taken. Little advertising signs used to promote the company name in retail stores are now sought after and serious collectors are also seeking out all the early sales literature.

One very special collectors piece which all visitors to the Collectors Centre are eligible to purchase is the model of Rose Cottage, Skirsgill, where the Lilliput Lane story began. As only a small proportion of the worldwide Club membership has the chance to make this 'pilgrimage' to the Lake District and few would part with this exclusive souvenir of a memorable day, it is a much coveted collectable.

DATING LILLIPUT LANE MODELS

There are three methods of dating a Lilliput Lane model: the design of the label on the base, the design of the packaging, and the company backstamp.

Labels

The label on the base can be used to identify the approximate age of a model. In the early days from 1982 to 1984, two types of label were used, one had a brown border and the other had a blue border. In 1985 the design of the label was changed with the company name featured prominently in the centre of the label. The labels include the name of the cottage and the words "Handmade in Cumbria UK (or United Kingdom). In the case of the different series, a distinguishing mark or symbol is used. For example, The American Landmarks series has an American flag on the label, and The Irish Collection is indicated by a shamrock in a banner under the words The Irish Collection.

Packaging

The design of the packaging has evolved since 1982 and should the model still have its original packaging then this can aid or even confirm the age of the model. Should a box be required for a model, then it is possible to purchase one of the current boxes through the retailer for a small charge.

Collectors always wonder whether a model is more valuable when it has its original box and its certificate (see page iv for an example) with it. With regard to certificates, certainly a limited edition or Collectors Club model should have its relevant certificate to show its provenance, and in the case of numbered editions a certificate is vital. However,with the other models many of the older ones did not have certificates with them when the model was produced.

Obviously, in an ideal world every collector would like to purchase a retired model complete with its original packaging and certificate. However, as this is not always possible, each collector must decide whether the model they wish to buy warrants the price being asked, or whether they should wait until they can purchase a model which is complete with the box and certificate. A model which does have its original box and certificate certainly will have added attractions to some collectors than a model on its own.

Backstamps

Backstamps are of great importance when dating a model. To make it easier for the collector to recognize the backstamp on their piece we have assigned a letter to each year that the cottages have been in production. Therefore, backstamp A refers to a cottage modelled in 1982, backstamp B refers to a cottage modelled in 1983, etc. The backstamps for a particular year may come in several sizes depending on the size of the base of the model. If the backstamp alters in appearance during a particular year we have indicated this by using the year's letter followed by a number. For example, in 1992 their was a backstamp with little dots on it and this is referred to as J-1. There was also a backstamp without the dots and this is referred to as J-2. All backstamps have the year of production indicated, as well as the Lilliput Lane logo with the copyright symbol (©), with the excecption of the models produced at the beginning of 1982 which only have the words "Lilliput Lane."

The backstamps from late-1982, 1983 and 1984 are all identical in appearance to the one shown below.

In 1985 and 1986 the backstamp shape was made more square in appearance. The Lilliput Lane wording was outlined (Lilliput Lane) for the first time.

In 1987 the backstamps took on a less structured shape, and this shape held for two years. 1989 saw the introduction of two backstamps. One was identical to the 1987 version but the second version (H-2) has a raised square border.

1987 Backstmap F

1984 Backstamp D

1989 Backstamp H-1

1990 was the first year that Lilliput Lane experimented with 'dots' on the backstamp. This dotted look also was available in 1991 and 1992.

1991 Backstamp J

The words "Lilliput Lane" on the 1993 backstamp were more straight in appearance than in the previous years. This also holds true for the 1994 backstamp.

1993 Backstamp L

A change in appearance of the backstamps took place during 1995 when letters EEGG were added after the date. This version is referred to as N-2 and is identical in appearance to the 1997 backstamp shown below. EEGG stands for Enesco European Giftware Group who purchased Lilliput Lane in 1995.

1997 Backstamp P

The design of the backstamp continued in 1998 and 1999 except for the year change.

1998 Backstamp Q

1999 Backstamp R

Backstamp	Issued
A-1	1982
A-2	1982
B	1983
C	1984
D	1985
E	1986
F	1987
G	1988
H-1	1989
H-2	1989
I-1	1990
I-2	1990
J	1991
K-1	1992

Backstamp	Issued
K-2	1992
L	1993
M	1994
N-1	1995
N-2	1995
O-1	1996
O-2	1996
O-3	1996
P-1	1997
P-2	1997
Q-1	1998
Q-2	1998
R	1999

INSURING YOUR COTTAGES

As with any other of your valuables, making certain your cottages are protected is a very important concern. It is paramount that you display or store any porcelain items is a secure place preferably one safely away from traffic in the home.

Your cottages are most often covered under your basic homeowner's policy and there are generally three kinds of such policies: standard, broad and comprehensive. Each has its own specific deductible and terms.

Under a general policy, your cottages are considered contents and are covered for all of the perils covered under the contractual terms of your policy (fire, theft, water damage and so on).

However, since cottages are extremely delicate, breakage is treated differently by most insurance companies. There is usually an extra premium attached to insure cottages against accidental breakage by or carelessness of the owner. This is sometimes referred to as a fine arts rider.

You are advised to contact your insurance professional to get all the answers.

In order to help you protect yourself, it is critical that you take inventory of your cottages and have colour photographs taken of all your pieces. This is the surest method of clearly establishing, for the police and your insurance company, the items lost or destroyed. It is also the easiest way to establish their replacement value in the event of a tragedy.

LILLIPUT LANE COLLECTORS CLUB

Details of membership are available from the following offices or from your local Lilliput Lane stockist:

UNITED KINGDOM
(and all other countries not listed below)
Lilliput Lane Collectors Club
Skirsgill, Penrith
Cumbria CA11 0DP
England
Telephone : +44 (0) 1768 212700
Fax: +44 (0) 1768 212601
Web site: www.lilliputlane.co.uk

U.S.A.
Lilliput Lane Collectors Club
P.O. Box 7
Libertytown, MD 21762-0007
U.S.A.
Telephone: (310) 829-8227 or (800) 545-5478
Fax: (301) 829-8554

CANADA
Lilliput Lane Collectors Club
7750 Tranmere Drive
Mississauga, Ontario L5S 1S6
Canada
Telephone: (905) 673-9200
Fax: (905) 673-7583

AUSTRALIA
Lilliput Lane Collectors Club
Locked Bag 30
Brunswick, MDC
Victoria 3056
Australia
Telephone: (03) 9381 2777
Fax: (03) 9381 9488

NEW ZEALAND
Lilliput Lane Collectors Club
P.O. Box 33-316
Petone, Wellington
New Zealand
Telephone: (04) 568 6619
Fax: (04) 568 6619

JAPAN
Lilliput Lane Collectors Club
Sanario Far East Company Ltd.
1-6-1 Osaki
Shinagawa-Ku
Tokyo 151
Japan
Telephone (03) 3779 8082
Fax: (03) 3779 8050

FURTHER READING

The Cottages of Lilliput Lane, Deborah Scott, Portfolio Press Corporation, 1991

The Pocket Guide to Lilliput Lane Cottages,™ 2nd Edition, Viv Marston, 2000.

Gulliver's World, published quarterly by the Lilliput Lane Collectors Club.

Lilliput Lane - The Complete Collectors Guide, Dan Komar, 1995.

AAN DE AMSTEL

Code No.:	128
Size:	5 ¾", 14.6 cm
Backstamp:	J
Introduced:	1991-1998
Varieties:	De Diamantair
Location:	Amsterdam
Series:	Netherlands
Can.	$75.00
U.S.	$60.00
U.K.	£30.00

Note: This model has a white roof and chimney.

ABERFORD GATE

Code No.:	Unknown
Size:	3 ½", 8.9 cm
Backstamp:	L
Introduced:	1993-1994
Location:	Aberford, Yorkshire
Series:	Special Editions
Can.	$175.00
U.S.	$110.00
U.K.	£ 75.00

"A CHERRY COKE™- JUST THE PRESCRIPTION"

Code No.:	895
Size:	3 ¼", 8.3 cm
Backstamp:	N-2
Introduced:	1995-1999
Location:	Silver Plume, Colorado
Series:	Coca-Cola™ Country
Can.	$165.00
U.S.	$100.00
U.K.	£ 65.00

ACORN COTTAGE

First Version (Cream)

Photograph not available at press time.

See next image for shape outline.

Code No.:	Unknown
Size:	2", 5.0 cm
Backstamp:	A-1
Introduced:	1982-1982
Series:	English: South-East
Can.	$900.00
U.S.	$600.00
U.K.	£375.00

ACORN COTTAGE

Second Version (Grey-blue with boulder)

Code No.:	Unknown
Size:	1 ¾", 4.4 cm
Backstamp:	A-1, A-2
Introduced:	1982-1984
Series:	English: South-East
Can.	$300.00
U.S.	$225.00
U.K.	£150.00

ACORN COTTAGE

Third Version (Grey-blue without boulder)

Code No.:	Unknown
Size:	2 ¼", 5.7 cm
Backstamp:	C
Introduced:	1984-1987
Series:	English: South-East
Can.	$125.00
U.S.	$100.00
U.K	£ 75.00

ADOBE CHURCH

Code No.:	Unknown
Size:	2 ¾", 7.0 cm
Backstamp:	C
Introduced:	1984-1985
Series:	American (1st)
Can.	$875.00
U.S.	$475.00
U.K.	£350.00

Note: Only 475 models were produced .

ADOBE VILLAGE
First Version (3 Crosses, 3 ladders)

Code No.:	Unknown
Size:	4 ¾", 12.1 cm
Backstamp:	C
Introduced:	1984-1985
Series:	American (1st)
Can.	$1,500.00
U.S.	$1,000.00
U.K.	£ 650.00

Note: Only 225 models of the Adobe Village in total were produced.

ADOBE VILLAGE
Second Version (1 Cross, no ladders)

Code No.:	Unknown
Size:	4 ¾", 12.1 cm
Backstamp:	C
Introduced:	1984-1985
Series:	American (1st)
Can.	$1,300.00
U.S.	$ 900.00
U.K.	£ 550.00

A DROP OF THE IRISH

Code No.:	L2332
Size:	3", 7.6 cm
Backstamp:	R
Introduced:	2000 to the present
Series	Irish
Can.	$95.00
U.S.	$65.00
U.K.	£25.95

AFTERNOON TEA

Code No.:	826
Size:	6", 15.0 cm
Backstamp:	N
Introduced:	1995 in a limited edition of 1,995
Location:	Carthage, Missouri
Series:	American Landmarks
Can.	$775.00
U.S.	$525.00
U.K.	£325.00

AIRA FORCE

Code No.:	L2326
Size:	2 ½", 6.4 cm
Backstamp:	R
Introduced:	2000 to the present
Series:	Visitor Centre Exclusive
Can.	N/A
U.S.	N/A
U.K.	£15.50

ALL SAINTS WATERMILLOCK

Code No.:	846
Size:	3 ¼″, 8.3 cm
Backstamp:	O-2
Introduced:	1996-1999
Location:	Watermillock, Cumbria
Series:	Lakeland Christmas
Can.	$55.00
U.S.	$35.00
U.K.	£20.00

THE ALMONRY

Code No.:	119
Size:	4 ¾″, 12.1 cm
Backstamp:	O-2
Introduced:	1996-1996
Location:	Evesham, Worcestershire
Series:	Special Editions
Can.	$400.00
U.S.	$250.00
U.K.	£175.00

ALTE SCHMIEDE

Code No.:	262
Size:	4 ½″, 11.9 cm
Backstamp:	K-1
Introduced:	1992-1998
Location:	Rothenburg, Germany
Series:	German
Can.	$140.00
U.S.	$100.00
U.K.	£ 55.00

AMAZING GRACE

Code No.:	L2279
Size:	4″, 10.1 cm
Backstamp:	R
Introduced:	1999 to the present
Series:	English
Can.	N/A
U.S.	$75.00
U.K.	£29.95

AMBERLEY ROSE

Code No.:	Unknown
Size:	3″, 7.6 cm
Backstamp:	O-2
Introduced:	1996-1997
Location:	Amberley, West Sussex
Series:	Special Editions
Can.	$135.00
U.S.	$ 90.00
U.K.	£ 60.00

Note: The original front door was cream, but customers could choose from a variety of colours.

AMISFIELD TOWER

Code No:	821
Size:	4 ¼″, 10.8 cm
Backstamp:	O-2
Introduced:	1995-1998
Location:	Nithsdale, Dumfrieshire
Series:	Scottish
Can.	$60.00
U.S.	$45.00
U.K.	£25.00

THE ANCHOR

Code No.: L2011
Size: 3 ¾", 9.5 cm
Backstamp: O-2
Introduced: 1996-2000
Location: Wingham, Kent
Series: English: South-East

Can. $100.00
U.S. $ 95.00
U.K. £ 29.95

ANNE HATHAWAY'S COTTAGE

Style One, First Version
(Name on base)

Code No.: Unknown
Size: 2 ¾", 7.0 cm
Backstamp: A-1
Introduced: 1983-1983
Location: Shottery
Series: English: Midlands

Can. $1,400.00
U.S. $1,000.00
U.K. £ 650.00

ANNE HATHAWAY'S COTTAGE

Style One, Second Version
(Without name on base)

Code No.: Unknown
Size: 2 ¾", 7.0 cm
Backstamp: B
Introduced: 1983-1984
Location: Shottery
Series: English: Midlands

Can. $425.00
U.S. $300.00
U.K. £200.00

Photograph not available at press time.

See image below for shape outline.

Photograph not available at press time.

See image below for shape outline.

ANNE HATHAWAY'S COTTAGE

Style One, Third Version
(Large chimney)

Code No: Unknown
Size: 2 ¾", 7.0 cm
Backstamp: C
Introduced: 1984-1988
Location: Shottery
Series: English: Midlands

Can. $150.00
U.S. $ 75.00
U.K. £ 65.00

ANNE HATHAWAY'S COTTAGE 1989

Style Two

Code No.: 191
Size: 3 ¼", 8.3 cm
Backstamp: H-1
Introduced: 1989-1997
Location: Shottery
Series: English: Midlands

Can. $150.00
U.S. $110.00
U.K. £ 75.00

ANNE OF CLEVES

Code No.: 603
Size: 5 ¾", 14.6 cm
Backstamp: J
Introduced: 1991-1996
Location: Ditchling, Sussex
Series: English: South-East

Can. $350.00
U.S. $225.00
U.K. £175.00

APOTHECARY

Code No.:	L2055
Size:	4", 10.1 cm
Backstamp:	P-1
Introduced:	1997-1999
Series:	Victorian Shops
Can.	$125.00
U.S.	$ 90.00
U.K.	£ 60.00

APPLEBY EAST

Code No.:	L2045
Size:	3 ¾", 9.5 cm
Backstamp:	P-1
Introduced:	1997-1999
Location:	Carlisle-Settle Railway Line
Series:	English
Can.	$90.00
U.S.	$70.00
U.K.	£45.00

APPLEJACK COTTAGE

Code No.:	699
Size:	2 ½", 6.4 cm
Backstamp:	M
Introduced:	1994-1999
Location:	Beaulieu, Hampshire
Series:	English: South-West
Can.	$50.00
U.S.	$35.00
U.K.	£20.00

APRIL COTTAGE

First Version (3 Pot chimney, thin timbers)

Code No.:	Unknown
Size:	2", 5.0 cm
Backstamp:	A-1
Introduced:	1982-1982
Location:	Hampshire
Series:	English: South-East
Can.	$750.00
U.S.	$500.00
U.K.	£350.00

Photograph not available at press time.

See next image for shape outline.

APRIL COTTAGE

Second Version (3 Pot chimney, thick timbers)

Code No.:	Unknown
Size:	1 ¾", 4.4 cm
Backstamp:	A-1, A-2
Introduced:	1982-1983
Location:	Hampshire
Series:	English: South-East
Can.	$450.00
U.S.	$300.00
U.K.	£200.00

APRIL COTTAGE

Third Version (2 Pot chimney, thick timbers)

Code No.:	Unknown
Size:	2 ½", 6.4 cm
Backstamp:	C
Introduced:	1983-1989
Location:	Hampshire
Series:	English: South-East
Can.	$125.00
U.S.	$ 85.00
U.K.	£ 60.00

ARBURY LODGE

Code No.: Unknown
Size: Unknown
Backstamp: P-1
Introduced: 1997-1997
Location: Nuneaton, Warwickshire
Series: Special Editions

Can. $175.00
U.S. $130.00
U.K. £ 90.00

Note: Available at the Lilliput Lane Collectors Event, June 7-8th, 1997.

ARMADA HOUSE

Code No.: 516
Size: 4 ¼", 10.8 cm
Backstamp: J
Introduced: 1991-1997
Location: Northamptonshire
Series: English: Midlands

Can. $165.00
U.S. $115.00
U.K. £ 75.00

ASHBERRY COTTAGE

Code No: Unknown
Size: 3 ½", 8.9 cm
Backstamp: K-1
Introduced: 1992 in a limited edition of 500
Varieties: Cranberry Cottage
Location: Minchin, Hampton Common, Gloucs.
Series: Special Editions

Can. $425.00
U.S. $275.00
U.K. £190.00

ASHLEIGH DOWN

Code No.: Unknown
Size: 3 ¼", 9.5 cm
Backstamp: L
Introduced: 1993-1994
Series: Paint Your Own

Can. $165.00
U.S. $120.00
U.K. £ 85.00

Note: Prices refer to unpainted models, which are more valuable.

ASH NOOK

Code No.: 046
Size: 3", 7.6 cm
Backstamp: H-1
Introduced: 1989-1995
Location: Hertfordshire
Series: English: South-East

Can. $80.00
U.S. $50.00
U.K. £35.00

L'AUBERGE D'ARMORIQUE

Code No.: 427
Size: 5 ½", 14.0 cm
Backstamp: I-2
Introduced: 1990-1997
Location: Brittany
Series: French

Can. $200.00
U.S. $125.00
U.K. £ 85.00

AUTUMN HUES

Code No.: 697
Size: 3 ½", 8.9 cm
Backstamp: M
Introduced: 1994-1997
Varieties: Spring Glory, Summer Impressions, Winter's Wonder
Location: Wiltshire
Series: Year in English Garden

Can. $85.00
U.S. $65.00
U.K. £35.00

THE BAKER'S SHOP

Code No.: 739
Size: 3 ½", 8.9 cm
Backstamp: N-1
Introduced: 1995-1999
Location: Broadway, Gloucestershire
Series: Village Shops

Can. $90.00
U.S. $65.00
U.K. £40.00

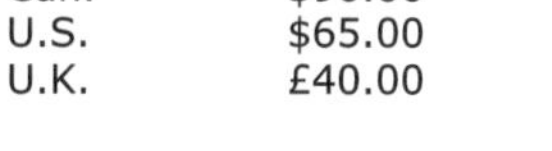

BALLYKERNE CROFT

Code No.: 068
Size: 2 ½", 6.4 cm
Backstamp: H-1
Introduced: 1989-1996
Location: County Galway
Series: Irish

Can. $90.00
U.S. $65.00
U.K. £45.00

BALMORAL

Code No.: L2288
Size: 4", 10.1 cm
Backstamp: R
Introduced: 2000 to the present
Location: Crathie, Scotland
Series: Britain's Heritage™: Royal Residences

Can. $160.00
U.S. $110.00
U.K. £ 45.95

"BANANAS ARE BACK!"

Code No.: L2198
Size: 4", 10.1 cm
Backstamp: Q-2
Introduced: 1998-1999
Series: Moments in Time

Can. $130.00
U.S. $ 70.00
U.K. £ 40.00

THE BANQUETING HOUSE

Code No.: 689
Size: 3", 7.6 cm
Backstamp: M
Introduced: 1994 in a limited edition of 5,000
Location: Ripon, Yorkshire
Series: Studley Royal

Can. $85.00
U.S. $55.00
U.K. £40.00

BARGATE COTTAGE TEA ROOM

Code No.:	773
Size:	4″, 10.1 cm
Backstamp:	N-1
Introduced:	1995-1999
Location:	Longleat Estate, Crocherton, Wiltshire
Series:	English Tea Rooms
Can.	$145.00
U.S.	$100.00
U.K.	£ 60.00

BAY VIEW

Code No.:	Unknown
Size:	2 ½″, 6.4 cm
Backstamp:	E
Introduced:	1986-1988
Location:	Burnham Market, Norfolk
Series:	English: South-East
Can.	$100.00
U.S.	$ 75.00
U.K.	£ 50.00

BEACON HEIGHTS

First Version (Less foliage)

Code No.:	Unknown
Size:	5 ¼″, 13.3 cm
Backstamp:	F
Introduced:	1987-1990
Location:	Northumberland
Series:	English: Northern
Can.	$225.00
U.S.	$150.00
U.K.	£100.00

BEACON HEIGHTS

Second Version (More foliage)

Code No.:	Unknown
Size:	5 ¼″, 13.3 cm
Backstamp:	F
Introduced:	1990-1992
Location:	Northumberland
Series:	English: Northern
Can.	$225.00
U.S.	$150.00
U.K.	£100.00

BEEHIVE COTTAGE

Code No.:	321
Size:	3 ¾″, 9.5 cm
Backstamp:	H-1
Introduced:	1989-1995
Location:	Cotswolds
Series:	English: Midlands
Can.	$100.00
U.S.	$ 75.00
U.K.	£ 50.00

BEEKEEPER'S COTTAGE

Code No.:	L2316
Size:	4 ¼″, 10.8 cm
Backstamp:	R
Introduced:	2000-2001
Series:	Collectors Club
Can.	$200.00
U.S.	N/A
U.K.	£ 54.95

BEGIJNHOF

Code No.:	126
Size:	4 ¾″, 12.1 cm
Backstamp:	J
Introduced:	1991-1998
Varieties:	De Pepermolen
Series:	Netherlands
Can.	$55.00
U.S.	$35.00
U.K.	£20.00

LA BERGERIE DU PÉRIGORD

Code No.:	429
Size:	5″, 12.7 cm
Backstamp:	I-2
Introduced:	1990-1997
Location:	Dordogne, France
Series:	French
Can.	$200.00
U.S.	$140.00
U.K.	£ 80.00

BERMUDA COTTAGE
First Variation (Blue)

Code No.:	Unknown
Size:	2″, 5.0 cm
Backstamp:	D
Introduced:	1985-1991
Location:	Bermuda
Series:	Special Edition
Can.	$525.00
U.S.	$350.00
U.K.	£200.00

Note: Begijnhof's roof is brown, while De Pepermolen's is grey and white.

BERMUDA COTTAGE
Second Variation (Pink)

Code No.:	Unknown
Size:	2″, 5.0 cm
Backstamp:	D
Introduced:	1985-1991
Location:	Bermuda
Series:	Special Edition
Can.	$375.00
U.S.	$225.00
U.K.	£150.00

BERMUDA COTTAGE
Third Variation (Yellow)

Code No.:	Unknown
Size:	2″, 5.0 cm
Backstamp:	D
Introduced:	1985-1991
Location:	Bermuda
Series:	Special Edition
Can.	$425.00
U.S.	$275.00
U.K.	£175.00

BESIDE THE SEASIDE

Code No.:	L2320
Size:	9 ½″, 24.0 cm
Backstamp:	R
Introduced:	2000 in a limited edition of 2,000
Can.	$2,400.00
U.S.	$2,000.00
U.K.	£ 650.00

BEST FRIENDS

Code No.: L2079
Size: Unknown
Backstamp: O-2
Introduced: 1997-1999
Location: Letcombe Basset, Oxfordshire
Series: English

Can. $35.00
U.S. $25.00
U.K. £15.00

BIG BEN

Code No.: L2211
Size: 8 ¾", 22.2 cm
Backstamp: Q-2
Introduced: 1998 to the present
Location: London
Series: Britain's Heritage™

Can $100.00
U.S. $ 75.00
U.K. £ 29.95

BIG BEN IN WINTER

Code No.: L2300
Size: 8 ¾", 22.2 cm
Backstamp: Q-2
Introduced: 1998-1999
Location: London
Series: Millennium

Can N/A
U.S. $80.00
U.K. £35.95

BILL AND BEN'S

Code No.: L2325
Size: 2 ¾", 7.0 cm
Backstamp: R
Introduced: 2000 to the present
Series: English

Can. $95.00
U.S. $65.00
U.K. £25.95

BIRCHWOOD COTTAGE

Code No.: L2014
Size: 3", 7.6 cm
Backstamp: O-2
Introduced: 1996-1998
Location: Amberley, West Sussex
Series: English: South-East

Can. $75.00
U.S. $50.00
U.K. £30.00

BIRDLIP BOTTOM

Code No.: 647
Size: 3 ¼", 8.3 cm
Backstamp: L
Introduced: 1993-1999
Location: Witcombe, Gloucestershire
Series: English: Midlands

Can. $80.00
U.S. $50.00
U.K. £35.00

THE BIRDSONG

Code No.: 680
Size: 3 ½", 8.9 cm
Backstamp: M
Introduced: 1994-1997
Series: American Landmarks

Can. $90.00
U.S. $60.00
U.K. £40.00

BIRTHDAY COTTAGE

Code No.: L2328
Size: 3 ¼", 8.3 cm
Backstamp: R
Introduced: 2000 to the present
Series: English

Can. $80.00
U.S. $50.00
U.K. £19.95

BLAIR ATHOLL

Code No.: Unknown
Size: 5", 12.7 cm
Backstamp: H-1
Introduced: 1989 in a limited edition of 3,000
Location: Pitlochery, Tayside
Series: Scottish

Can. $450.00
U.S. $325.00
U.K. £225.00

Note: Early versions were patchy on the white areas of the building.

BLOEMENMARKT

Code No.: 129
Size: 6 ¼", 15.9 cm
Backstamp: J
Introduced: 1991-1998
Varieties: De Zijdewever
Series: Netherlands

Can. $90.00
U.S. $60.00
U.K. £30.00

Note: The basement door on Bloemenmarkt is brown, while De Zijdewever's is red.

BLUE BOAR

Code No.: 008
Size: 3 ¾", 9.5 cm
Backstamp: O-1
Introduced: 1996-1999
Location: Chievely
Series: English: South-East

Can. $110.00
U.S. $ 75.00
U.K. £ 50.00

BLUEBELL FARM

Code No.: L2013
Size: 4", 10.1 cm
Backstamp: O-3
Introduced: 1996-1999
Varieties: First Snow at Bluebell
Location: Hanlith, North Yorkshire
Series: English: Northern

Can. $300.00
U.S. $225.00
U.K. £150.00

THE BOBBINS

Code No.: L2178
Size: 3 ½", 8.9 cm
Backstamp: Q-2
Introduced: 1998 to the present
Series: English

Can. $130.00
U.S. $ 85.00
U.K. £ 35.95

BOBBY BLUE

Code No.: L2176
Size: 3 ¾", 9.5 cm
Backstamp: Q-2
Introduced: 1998 to the present
Series: English

Can. $180.00
U.S. $120.00
U.K. £ 45.95

BODIAM

Code No.: 686
Size: 3", 7.6 cm
Backstamp: M
Introduced: 1994-1997
Location: Sussex
Series: Historic Castles of Britain

Can. $125.00
U.S. $ 85.00
U.K. £ 60.00

BO-PEEP TEA ROOMS

Code No.: 800
Size: 3", 7.6 cm
Backstamp: N-1
Introduced: 1995-1997
Location: Bourton-on-the-Water, Gloucestershire
Series: English Tea Rooms

Can. $125.00
U.S. $ 85.00
U.K. £ 60.00

BOOK SHOP

Code No.: L2051
Size: 5", 12.7 cm
Backstamp: P-1
Introduced: 1997-1999
Location: Keswick, Cumbria
Series: Victorian Shops

Can. $95.00
U.S. $65.00
U.K. £40.00

BORROWDALE SCHOOL

Code No.: 845
Size: 2 ½", 6.4 cm
Backstamp: O-2
Introduced: 1996-1999
Location: Crostwaite, Cumbria
Series: Lakeland Christmas

Can. $55.00
U.S. $35.00
U.K. £20.00

BOTTLE OF CHEER

Code No.:	L2280
Size:	2 ½", 6.4 cm
Backstamp:	R
Introduced:	1999 to the present
Series:	English
Can.	N/A
U.S.	$25.00
U.K.	£ 9.95

BOW COTTAGE

Code No.:	617
Size:	3 ½", 8.9 cm
Backstamp:	K-1
Introduced:	1992-1995
Location:	Badminton, Gloucestershire
Series:	English: Midlands
Can.	$150.00
U.S.	$100.00
U.K.	£ 60.00

BOWBEAMS

Code No.:	L2141
Size:	3 ¾", 9.5 cm
Backstamp:	P-1
Introduced:	1998-1999
Location:	West Tarring, West Sussex
Series:	English
Can.	$300.00
U.S.	$175.00
U.K.	£125.00

BOXWOOD COTTAGE

Code No.:	L2002
Size:	2 ½", 6.4 cm
Backstamp:	O-2
Introduced:	1996-1999
Location:	Minstead, Hampshire
Series:	English: South-East
Can.	$45.00
U.S.	$30.00
U.K.	£20.00

BRAMBLE COTTAGE

Code No.:	507
Size:	3 ¼", 8.3 cm
Backstamp:	I-1
Introduced:	1990-1995
Location:	Berkshire
Series:	English: Midlands
Can.	$95.00
U.S.	$65.00
U.K.	£40.00

DE BRANDERIJ

Code No.:	127
Size:	5 ¼", 13.3 cm
Backstamp:	J
Introduced:	1991-1998
Varieties:	De Wolhandelaar
Series:	Netherlands
Can.	$75.00
U.S.	$50.00
U.K.	£30.00

Note: De Branderij's roof is white, while De Wolhandelaar's is grey.

BRECON BACH

Code No.:	142
Size:	3", 7.6 cm
Backstamp:	E
Introduced:	1986-1993
Location:	Brecon Beacons, Wales
Series:	Welsh
Can.	$95.00
U.S.	$65.00
U.K.	£40.00

BREDON HOUSE

Code No.:	200
Size:	4 ¼", 10.8 cm
Backstamp:	G
Introduced:	1988-1990
Location:	Stratford-upon-Avon
Series:	English: Midlands
Can.	$200.00
U.S.	$145.00
U.K.	£100.00

THE BRIARY

Code No.:	050
Size:	2 ¾", 7.0 cm
Backstamp:	H-1
Introduced:	1989-1995
Location:	Stourhead, Wiltshire
Series:	English: South-West
Can.	$95.00
U.S.	$60.00
U.K.	£40.00

BRIDGE HOUSE
First Version

Code No.:	Unknown
Size:	2 ½", 6.4 cm
Backstamp:	None
Introduced:	1982-1990
Location:	Ambleside, Cumbria
Series:	English: Northern
Can.	$75.00
U.S.	$50.00
U.K.	£30.00

Note: Inscribed "BRIDGE HOUSE" at foot of bridge.

BRIDGE HOUSE 1991
Second Version

Code No.:	022
Size:	3", 7.6 cm
Backstamp:	None
Introduced:	1991-1998
Location:	Ambleside, Cumbria
Series:	English: Northern
Can.	$30.00
U.S.	$20.00
U.K.	£15.00

Note: Inscribed "BRIDGE HOUSE 1991". Slightly larger and more refined.

BRIDGE HOUSE
Third Version

Code No.:	Unknown
Size:	1 ½", 3.9 cm
Backstamp:	None
Introduced:	1997-1999
Location:	Ambleside, Cumbria
Series:	Dream Cottage Miniatures
Can.	$25.00
U.S.	$16.00
U.K.	£10.00

BRIDGE HOUSE IN WINTER

Code No.:	Unknown
Size:	3", 7.6 cm
Backstamp:	None
Introduced:	1995 in a limited edition of 3,000
Location:	Ambleside, Cumbria
Series:	1. English: Northern 2. Special Edition

Can.	$65.00
U.S.	$50.00
U.K.	£30.00

BRIDGE HOUSE DEALER SIGN

First Version

Code No.:	Unknown
Size:	2 ½", 6.4 cm
Backstamp:	None
Introduced:	1982-1982
Location:	Ambleside, Cumbria
Series:	1. Dealer Sign 2. Special Edition

Can.	$975.00
U.S.	$675.00
U.K.	£450.00

Note: Later replaced by a flat-back version.

BRIDGE HOUSE DEALER SIGN

Second Version, First Variation (Thick)

Code No.:	Unknown
Size:	4", 10.1 cm
Backstamp:	None
Introduced:	1983-1983
Location:	Ambleside, Cumbria
Series:	1. Dealer Sign 2. Special Edition

Can.	$700.00
U.S.	$500.00
U.K.	£300.00

BRIDGE HOUSE DEALER SIGN

Second Version, Second Variation (Thin)

Code No.:	Unknown
Size:	4", 10.1 cm
Backstamp:	None
Introduced:	1983-1984
Location:	Ambleside, Cumbria
Series:	1. Dealer Sign 2. Special Edition

Can.	$500.00
U.S.	$350.00
U.K.	£225.00

BRIDLE WAY

Code No.:	Unknown
Size:	3 ¾", 9.5 cm
Backstamp:	H-1
Introduced:	1990-1991
Location:	Oxfordshire
Series:	Collectors Club

Can.	$200.00
U.S.	$150.00
U.K.	£100.00

BRO DAWEL

Code No.:	434
Size:	2", 5.0 cm
Backstamp:	J
Introduced:	1991-1998
Location:	Dyfed, Wales
Series:	Welsh

Can.	$45.00
U.S.	$30.00
U.K.	£15.00

BROCKBANK

Code No.:	053
Size:	3 ½″, 8.9 cm
Backstamp:	G
Introduced:	1988-1993
Location:	Surrey
Series:	English: South-East
Can.	$95.00
U.S.	$65.00
U.K.	£40.00

BRONTË PARSONAGE
First Version (Thin surrounds)

Code No.:	Unknown
Size:	3 ¾″, 9.5 cm
Backstamp:	D
Introduced:	1985-1985
Location:	Haworth, Yorkshire
Series:	English: Northern
Can.	$700.00
U.S.	$500.00
U.K.	£325.00

BRONTË PARSONAGE
Second Version (Thick surrounds)

Code No.:	Unknown
Size:	3 ¾″, 9.5 cm
Backstamp:	D
Introduced:	1985-1987
Location:	Haworth, Yorkshire
Series:	English: Northern
Can.	$225.00
U.S.	$150.00
U.K.	£100.00

Photograph not available at press time.

See next image for shape outline.

DER BÜCHERWURM

Code No.:	264
Size:	4 ¼″, 10.8 cm
Backstamp:	K-1
Introduced:	1992-1998
Location:	Tübingen, Germany
Series:	German
Can.	$125.00
U.S.	$ 85.00
U.K.	£ 60.00

BUCKINGHAM PALACE

Code No.:	L2286
Size:	2 ¾″, 7.0 cm
Backstamp:	R
Introduced:	1999 to the present
Location:	London
Series:	Britain's Heritage™: Royal Residences
Can.	N/A
U.S.	$100.00
U.K.	£ 39.95

BUCKLE MY SHOE

Code No.:	L2186
Size:	4″, 10.1 cm
Backstamp:	Q-2
Introduced:	1998-2000
Location:	London
Series:	English
Can.	$130.00
U.S.	$ 85.00
U.K.	£ 39.95

BUCKLE YEAT™

Code No.:	L2272
Size:	3", 7.6 cm
Backstamp:	R
Introduced:	1999 to the present
Series:	Beatrix Potter™
Can.	N/A
U.S.	$95.00
U.K.	£39.95

BUMBLE BEE COTTAGE

Code No.:	L2041
Size:	2 ¼", 5.7 cm
Backstamp:	P-1
Introduced:	1997-1999
Location:	Treworthal, Cornwall
Series:	English
Can.	$50.00
U.S.	$35.00
U.K.	£20.00

BURLEY STREET GARAGE

Code No.:	L2335
Size:	3 ½", 8.9 cm
Backstamp:	R
Introduced:	2000 to the present
Series:	English
Can.	$280.00
U.S.	$170.00
U.K.	£ 65.95

BURNS' COTTAGE, ALLOWAY

Code No.:	Unknown
Size:	2", 5.0 cm
Backstamp:	D
Introduced:	1985-1988
Location:	Alloway, Scotland
Series:	Scottish
Can.	$175.00
U.S.	$125.00
U.K.	£ 85.00

BURNSIDE

First Variation (Grey chimney)

Code No.:	Unknown
Size:	2 ½", 6.4 cm
Backstamp:	A-1
Introduced:	1982-1982
Location:	Glenridding
Series:	English: Northern
Can.	$900.00
U.S.	$600.00
U.K.	£400.00

BURNSIDE

Second Variation (Sienna chimney)

Code No.:	Unknown
Size:	2 ¼", 5.7 cm
Backstamp:	A-2
Introduced:	1982-1985
Location:	Glenridding
Series:	English: Northern
Can.	$650.00
U.S.	$450.00
U.K.	£300.00

BURNSIDE

Third Variation (Right rear backstamp)

Code No.:	Unknown
Size:	2 ¼", 5.7 cm
Backstamp:	B
Introduced:	1985-1985
Location:	Glenridding
Series:	English: Northern
Can.	$525.00
U.S.	$375.00
U.K.	£250.00

BUTTERCUP COTTAGE

Code No.:	Unknown
Size:	2 ¾", 7.0 cm
Backstamp:	I-1
Introduced:	1990-1992
Location:	Gloucestershire
Series:	English: Midlands
Can.	$70.00
U.S.	$45.00
U.K.	£30.00

BUTTERFLY COTTAGE

Code No.:	L2298
Size:	3", 7.6 cm
Backstamp:	R
Introduced:	1999-2000
Series:	Sales Promotion Special Edition
Can.	N/A
U.S.	$70.00
U.K.	£24.95

BUTTERMILK FARM

Code No.:	L2099
Size:	4", 10.1 cm
Backstamp:	P-1
Introduced:	1997-2000
Location:	Tivington, Somerset
Series:	English
Can.	$175.00
U.S.	$120.00
U.K.	£ 80.00

BUTTERWICK

Code No.:	148
Size:	2 ¾", 7.0 cm
Backstamp:	H-1
Introduced:	1989-1996
Location:	North Devon
Series:	English: South-West
Can.	$75.00
U.S.	$50.00
U.K.	£35.00

BUTTON DOWN

Code No.:	790
Size:	2 ½", 6.4 cm
Backstamp:	N-1
Introduced:	1995-1998
Location:	Gloucestershire
Series:	English: Midlands
Can.	$45.00
U.S.	$30.00
U.K.	£20.00

BWTHYN BACH GWYN (LITTLE WHITE COTTAGE)

Code No.: L2160
Size: 2 ½", 6.4 cm
Backstamp: P-2
Introduced: 1998 to the present
Location: Merthyr Mawr, Wales
Series: Welsh

Can. $65.00
U.S. $35.00
U.K. £17.50

BY DAWN'S EARLY LIGHT

Code No.: L2162
Size: 3 ¾", 9.5 cm
Backstamp: Unknown
Introduced: 1998 to the present
Location: Puget Sound, Washington
Series: Allegiance

Can. N/A
U.S. $70.00
U.K. £29.95

LA CABANE DU GARDIAN

Code No.: 422
Size: 2", 5.0 cm
Backstamp: I-2
Introduced: 1990-1997
Location: Camargue, France
Series: French

Can. $65.00
U.S. $50.00
U.K. £30.00

CALENDAR COTTAGE

Code No.: L2008
Size: 3 ¼", 8.3 cm
Backstamp: O-2
Introduced: 1996-1999
Location: Amberley, West Sussex
Series: English: South-East

Can. $65.00
U.S. $50.00
U.K. £30.00

CAMOMILE LAWN

Code No.: 668
Size: 3 ¼", 8.3 cm
Backstamp: M
Introduced: 1994-1997
Location: Therfield, Hertfordshire
Series: English: South-East

Can. $120.00
U.S. $ 80.00
U.K. £ 50.00

CAMPDEN COT

Code No.: L2184
Size: 2 ¾", 7.0 cm
Backstamp: Q-2
Introduced: 1998 to the present
Series: English

Can. $60.00
U.S. $35.00
U.K. £15.50

CANDY COTTAGE

Code No.:	L2327
Size:	3 ¾", 9.5 cm
Backstamp:	R
Introduced:	2000-2000
Series:	Sales Promotion Special Edition
Can.	N/A
U.S.	$65.00
U.K.	£26.95

CANTERBURY BELLS

Code No.:	L2101
Size:	3 ½", 8.9 cm
Backstamp:	P-1
Introduced:	1997-1999
Location:	Weald, Kent
Series:	English
Can.	$200.00
U.S.	$150.00
U.K.	£ 95.00

CAPE COD COTTAGE

Code No.:	Unknown
Size:	2 ½", 6.4 cm
Backstamp:	C
Introduced:	1984-1985
Series:	American (1st)
Can.	$550.00
U.S.	$375.00
U.K.	£250.00

Note: Only 225 models were produced.

CARRICK HOUSE

Code No.:	485
Size:	2 ½", 6.4 cm
Backstamp:	H-1
Introduced:	1989-1998
Series:	Scottish
Can.	$60.00
U.S.	$40.00
U.K.	£25.00

CASTELL COCH

First Version (With knobs)

Code No.:	687A
Size:	5 ½", 14.0 cm
Backstamp:	M
Introduced:	1994-1994
Location:	Near Cardiff, Wales
Series:	1. Historic Castles of Britain 2. Welsh
Can.	$300.00
U.S.	$200.00
U.K.	£125.00

CASTELL COCH

Second Version (Without knobs)

Code No.:	687B
Size:	5 ½", 14.0 cm
Backstamp:	O
Introduced:	1994-1999
Location:	Near Cardiff, Wales
Series:	1. Historic Castles of Britain 2. Welsh
Can.	$200.00
U.S.	$120.00
U.K.	£ 65.00

CASTLE STREET
First Version (Engraved name)

Code No.: Unknown
Size: 5 ½", 14.0 cm
Backstamp: A-1, A-2
Introduced: 1982-1984
Series: English: Northern

Can. $550.00
U.S. $400.00
U.K. £250.00

CASTLE STREET
Second Version (Embossed name)

Code No.: Unknown
Size: 5 ½", 14.0 cm
Backstamp: B, C
Introduced: 1984-1986
Series: English: Northern

Can. $550.00
U.S. $400.00
U.K. £250.00

THE CAT'S WHISKERS

Code No.: L2275
Size: 3 ½", 8.9 cm
Backstamp: R
Introduced: 1999 to the present
Series: English

Can. N/A
U.S. $85.00
U.K. £35.95

Photograph not available at press time.

See next image for shape outline.

CATKIN COTTAGE

Code No.: L2089
Size: 3", 7.6 cm
Backstamp: P-1
Introduced: 1997-2000
Location: Woolston, Devon
Series: English

Can. $100.00
U.S. $ 70.00
U.K. £ 28.50

CATMINT COTTAGE

Code No.: L2134
Size: 3", 7.6 cm
Backstamp: Q-2
Introduced: 1998
Series: Paint Your Own

Can. $45.00
U.S. $30.00
U.K. £20.00

Note: Prices refer to unpainted models, which are more valuable.

CATS COOMBE COTTAGE

Code No.: 154
Size: 2 ¾", 7.0 cm
Backstamp: L
Introduced: 1993-1995
Location: Wool, Dorset
Series: English: South-West

Can. $95.00
U.S. $65.00
U.K. £40.00

CAWDOR CASTLE

Code No.: Unknown
Size: 6", 15.0 cm
Backstamp: I-2
Introduced: 1990 in a limited edition of 3,000
Location: Inverness, Scotland
Series: Scottish

Can. $700.00
U.S. $475.00
U.K. £300.00

CHALFONT ST. GILES

Code No.: L2203
Size: 4 ¼", 10.8 cm
Backstamp: R
Introduced: 1999-1999
Series: Helen Allingham

Can. $220.00
U.S. $150.00
U.K. £ 60.00

CHALK DOWN

Code No.: L2005
Size: 2 ½", 6.4 cm
Backstamp: O-2
Introduced: 1996-1999
Location: Amberley, West Sussex
Series: English: South-East

Can. $45.00
U.S. $35.00
U.K. £20.00

Photograph not available at press time.

See next image for shape outline.

CHANTRY CHAPEL

First Version (Spires - 2 cm)

Code No.: Unknown
Size: 4 ¼", 10.8 cm
Backstamp: G
Introduced: 1988-1988
Location: Wakefield
Series: Special Edition

Can. $375.00
U.S. $250.00
U.K. £170.00

CHANTRY CHAPEL

Second Version (Spires - 3 cm)

Code No.: Unknown
Size: 4", 10.1 cm
Backstamp: G
Introduced: 1988-1991
Location: Wakefield
Series: Special Edition

Can. $450.00
U.S. $300.00
U.K. £200.00

Note: Remodelled due to breakage problems.

CHATSWORTH BLOOMS

Code No.: L2174
Size: 3 ½", 8.9 cm
Backstamp: Q-2
Introduced: 1998-2000
Series: English

Can. N/A
U.S. $120.00
U.K. £ 45.95

CHATSWORTH VIEW

Code No.: 604
Size: 5″, 12.7 cm
Backstamp: J
Introduced: 1991-1996
Location: Edensor, Derbyshire
Series: English: Northern

Can. $225.00
U.S. $165.00
U.K. £100.00

CHATTERBOX CORNER

Code No.: L2333
Size: 3 ½″, 8.9 cm
Backstamp: R
Introduced: 2000 to the present
Series: English

Can. $120.00
U.S. $ 75.00
U.K. £ 29.95

LA CHAUMIÉRE DU VERGER

Code No.: 424
Size: 3 ¼″, 8.3 cm
Backstamp: I-2
Introduced: 1990-1997
Location: Normandy Coast
Series: French

Can. $100.00
U.S. $ 75.00
U.K. £ 50.00

CHERRY BLOSSOM COTTAGE

Code No.: 777
Size: 3 ½″, 8.9 cm
Backstamp: N-1
Introduced: 1995-1997
Location: Barton Mills, Suffolk
Series: English: South-East

Can. $1250.00
U.S. $ 80.00
U.K. £ 50.00

CHERRY COTTAGE

Code No.: 411
Size: 2 ¾″, 7.0 cm
Backstamp: I-2
Introduced: 1990-1995
Location: Suffolk
Series: English: South-East

Can. $60.00
U.S. $40.00
U.K. £25.00

CHESTNUT COTTAGE

Code No.: 625
Size: 2 ½″, 6.4 cm
Backstamp: K-1
Introduced: 1992-1996
Location: Bilbury, Gloucestershire
Series: Christmas

Can. $45.00
U.S. $30.00
U.K. £20.00

CHILTERN MILL

Code No.:	517
Size:	6 ¾", 17.2 cm
Backstamp:	H-1
Introduced:	1989-1995
Series:	English: Midlands
Can.	$125.00
U.S.	$ 80.00
U.K.	£ 50.00

THE CHINA SHOP

Code No.:	740
Size:	3 ½", 8.9 cm
Backstamp:	N-1
Introduced:	1995-1999
Location:	Burford, Oxfordshire
Series:	Village Shops
Can.	$120.00
U.S.	$ 85.00
U.K.	£ 40.00

CHINE COT

First Version (Grey Steps)

Code No.:	032A
Size:	2 ½", 6.4 cm
Backstamp:	H-1
Introduced:	1987-1989
Location:	Isle of Wight
Series:	English: South-East
Can.	$100.00
U.S.	$ 75.00
U.K.	£ 50.00

Note: The front and back doors originally had glass effect panes

CHINE COT

Second Version (Buff steps)

Code No.:	032B
Size:	2 ½", 6.4 cm
Backstamp:	H-1
Introduced:	1989-1996
Location:	Isle of Wight
Series:	English: South-East
Can.	$50.00
U.S.	$35.00
U.K.	£20.00

Note: Four windows were bricked up, and the doors became solid.

CHIPPING COOMBE

Code No.:	779
Size:	5 ½", 14.0 cm
Backstamp:	Special Limited Edition
Introduced:	1995 in a limited edition of 3,000
Location:	Castle Coombe, Wiltshire
Series:	English: South-West
Can.	$725.00
U.S.	$525.00
U.K.	£395.00

THE CHOCOLATE HOUSE

First Version - 4 ½"

Code No.:	632
Size:	4 ½", 11.9 cm
Backstamp:	K-1
Introduced:	1992-1998
Location:	Kendal, Cumbria
Series:	English: Northern
Can.	$125.00
U.S.	$ 80.00
U.K.	£ 50.00

THE CHOCOLATE HOUSE
Second Version - 1 ½″

Code No.:	Unknown
Size:	1 ½″, 3.9 cm
Backstamp:	None
Introduced:	1997-1999
Location:	Kendal, Cumbria
Series:	Dream Cottage Miniatures
Can.	$45.00
U.S.	$30.00
U.K.	£20.00

CHRISTMAS PARTY

Code No.:	L2060
Size:	4″, 10.1 cm
Backstamp:	P-1
Introduced:	1997-1997
Location:	Derbyshire
Series:	Christmas Specials
Can.	$125.00
U.S.	$100.00
U.K.	£ 60.00

CIDER APPLE COTTAGE

Code No.:	L2043
Size:	3 ¾″, 9.5 cm
Backstamp:	P-1
Introduced:	1997-1998
Location:	Selworthy
Series:	Collectors Club
Can.	$65.00
U.S.	$45.00
U.K.	£30.00

CIRCULAR COTTAGE
First Version - 4 ½″

Code No.:	Unknown
Size:	4 ½″, 11.9 cm
Backstamp:	H-1
Introduced:	1989-1993
Location:	Bristol
Series:	Blaise Hamlet
Can.	$175.00
U.S.	$125.00
U.K.	£ 80.00

CIRCULAR COTTAGE
Second Version - 2 ½″

Code No.:	Unknown
Size:	2 ½″, 6.4 cm
Backstamp:	L
Introduced:	1993-1995
Location:	Bristol
Series:	Classics
Can.	$95.00
U.S.	$65.00
U.K.	£40.00

CLARE COTTAGE

Code No.:	Unknown
Size:	3″, 7.6 cm
Backstamp:	D
Introduced:	1985-1993
Location:	Clare, Suffolk
Series:	English: South-East
Can.	$60.00
U.S.	$40.00
U.K.	£25.00

CLAYPOTTS CASTLE

Code No.: 481
Size: 5", 12.7 cm
Backstamp: H-1
Introduced: 1989-1997
Location: Dundee
Series: Scottish

Can. $95.00
U.S. $70.00
U.K. $45.00

CLEY-NEXT-THE-SEA

First Variation (Red boat)

Code No.: 638A
Size: 8 ½", 21.6 cm
Backstamp: K-1
Introduced: 1992 in a limited editionof 150 for the USA
Location: Blakeney Harbour, Norfolk
Series: English: South-East

Can. $1,000.00
U.S. $ 750.00
U.K. £ 500.00

CLEY-NEXT-THE-SEA

Second Variation (Yellow boat)

Code No.: 638B
Size: 8 ½", 21.6 cm
Backstamp: K-1
Introduced: 1992 in a limited edition of 2,850 for the Collectors Club
Location: Blakeney Harbour, Norfolk
Series: English: South-East

Can. $750.00
U.S. $500.00
U.K. £350.00

CLIBURN SCHOOL

Code No.: Unknown
Size: 2 ½", 6.4 cm
Backstamp: A-1
Introduced: 1983 in a limited edition of 64
Varieties: Old School House
Location: Cliburn Village
Series: Special Editions

Can. $5,000.00
U.S. $4,000.00
U.K. £2,500.00

CLOCKMAKER'S COTTAGE

Code No.: Unknown
Size: 4", 10.1 cm
Backstamp: F
Introduced: 1987-1990
Series: Special Edition

Can. $350.00
U.S. $250.00
U.K. £175.00

CLOVER COTTAGE

First Variation (Orange Foliage)

Code No.: 302A
Size: 2", 5.0 cm
Backstamp: F
Introduced: 1987-1988
Location: Devon
Series: English: South-West

Can. $95.00
U.S. $75.00
U.K. £50.00

CLOVER COTTAGE
Second Variation (Green Foliage)

Code No.:	302B
Size:	2 ½″, 6.4 cm
Backstamp:	G
Introduced:	1988-1994
Location:	Devon
Series:	English: South-West
Can.	$45.00
U.S.	$30.00
U.K.	£20.00

THE COACH AND HORSES

Code No.:	L2112
Size:	5″, 12.7 cm
Backstamp:	P-1
Introduced:	1997-2000
Location:	Brunton Street, London
Series:	English
Can.	$150.00
U.S.	$ 90.00
U.K.	£ 45.95

COACH HOUSE
First Version (Pathway, Criss-Cross Lattice)

Code No.:	Unknown
Size:	4″, 10.1 cm
Backstamp:	None
Introduced:	1982-1982
Series:	English: South-East
Can.	$2,000.00
U.S.	$1,500.00
U.K.	£ 950.00

Note: 67 models were produced.

Photograph not available at press time.

See previous image for shape outline.

COACH HOUSE
Second Version (No Pathway, Tudor Panelling)

Code No.:	Unknown
Size:	4″, 10.1 cm
Backstamp:	A-1, A-2
Introduced:	1982-1985
Series:	English: South-East
Can.	$950.00
U.S.	$650.00
U.K.	£425.00

Note: 803 models were produced.

COBBLERS COTTAGE

Code No.:	143
Size:	2 ½″, 6.4 cm
Backstamp:	E
Introduced:	1986-1994
Location:	Northamptonshire
Series:	English: Midlands
Can.	$90.00
U.S.	$60.00
U.K.	£40.00

COCKLESHELLS

Code No.:	L2088
Size:	2″, 5.0 cm
Backstamp:	P-1
Introduced:	1997-2000
Location:	Hope Cove, Devon
Series:	English
Can.	$40.00
U.S.	$25.00
U.K.	£ 9.95

COMFORT COTTAGE

Code No.:	L2127
Size:	2 ½", 6.4 cm
Backstamp:	Q-2
Introduced:	1998-1999
Series:	Collectors Club
Can.	$65.00
U.S.	$50.00
U.K.	£30.00

CONISTON CRAG

Code No.:	L2169
Size:	6 ¾", 17.2 cm
Backstamp:	Q-2
Introduced:	1998 in a limited edition of 3,000
Can.	$1,200.00
U.S.	$ 750.00
U.K.	£ 350.00

CONVENT IN THE WOODS

Code No.:	418
Size:	4 ½", 11.9 cm
Backstamp:	I-2
Introduced:	1990-1996
Location:	Mere, Wltshire
Series:	English: South-West
Can.	$225.00
U.S.	$165.00
U.K.	£100.00

COOPERS

First Version - 3 ½"

Code No.:	Unknown
Size:	3 ½", 8.9 cm
Backstamp:	A-1
Introduced:	1983-1983
Location:	West Sussex
Series:	English: South-East
Can.	$700.00
U.S.	$500.00
U.K.	£300.00

COOPERS

Second Version - 2 ¾")

Code No.:	Unknown
Size:	2 ¾", 7.0 cm
Backstamp:	A-2
Introduced:	1983-1986
Location:	West Sussex
Series:	English: South-East
Can.	$450.00
U.S.	$300.00
U.K.	£200.00

Note: Base appears more pitted.

CORNFLOWER COTTAGE

Code No.:	Unknown
Size:	3 ¼", 8.3 cm
Backstamp:	O-2
Introduced:	1996-1996
Location:	Cuddington, Buckinghamshire
Series:	Special Editions
Can.	$200.00
U.S.	$145.00
U.K.	£ 90.00

THE AMERICAN LANDMARKS COLLECTION by Ray Day

Afternoon Tea: Introduced in June 1995 in a limited edition of 1,995. This model was based on a building in Carthage, Missouri that was built in c.1810.

The Birdsong: This model depicting the American Midwest roadside barn, was available only in North America during 1994 before general release in 1995.

Country Church: This typical American church, built in Shelbyville, Indiana c.1872, was demolished in 1991. *Country Church* was released in 1989.

Covered Memories: Based upon a renowned wooden covered bridge, *Covered Memories* was introduced in 1990 in the USA. It was released worldwide the following year.

THE AMERICAN LANDMARKS COLLECTION by Ray Day

Fire House 1: Constructed c.1890, this Maine building illustrates Victorian architectural influences. It was sold exclusively in the USA the first year of issue.

Fresh Bread: Located in Silver Plume, Colorado, *Fresh Bread* served the specialist grocery needs of migrants flocking west in search of their fortunes c.1850.

Great Point Light: Built in 1818, this lighthouse stood until 1984, when it fell in a severe storm. The model was released March 1990.

Harvest Mill: Introduced in January 1994 in a limited edition of 3,500, this model was based on the Old Mill at Pigeon Forge, Tennessee.

THE AMERICAN LANDMARKS COLLECTION by Ray Day

Gold Miner's Claim , First Version (Without snow) **Gold Miner's Claim, Second Version (With snow)**
First released in 1992 *Gold Miner's Claim* illustrates the disused mine, derelict cabin and rusting equipment left behind by prospectors after the mine had run out. Approximately 15 pieces were released from the factory without snow.

Holy Night: Constructed in 1887 in Louisville, Kentucky, this church was built for $20,000.00 and has been serving the community ever since.

Home for the Holidays: *Home for the Holidays* was released in 1996 in a limited edition of 2,595. The buildings are typical of 1820s Indiana and Illinois.

THE AMERICAN LANDMARKS COLLECTION by Ray Day

Home Sweet Home: This model, released in 1992, illustrates the type of construction familiar to so many colonists in America - the log cabin.

Lobster at the Pier: Introduced in 1997, *Lobster at the Pier* is typical of the restaurants found in fishing ports along the New England coastline.

Mail Pouch Barn: Located on Highway 36, west of Indianapolis, Indiana, this model is a typical tobacco factory at which mail carriers would often stop.

Nature's Bounty: Commemorating the 10th anniversary of the *American Landmarks Collection* in 1999, this piece is based upon Wayside Inn Gristmill in Sudbury, Massachusetts.

THE AMERICAN LANDMARKS COLLECTION by Ray Day

Rambling Rose: This model is typical of the buildings in the Massachusetts summer resort of Nantucket Island. It was released in 1991.

Roadside Coolers: Built around 1890 in Huron, Indiana, *Roadside Coolers* is a typical general store. This model was sold exclusively in the USA the first year of issue.

School Days: A one-room school house, this model was based on school houses seen throughout 19th century America.

See Rock City: Built at the top of Lookout Mountain in the Appalachians, visitors can see not only Rock City, but seven of the American states.

THE AMERICAN LANDMARKS COLLECTION by Ray Day

Seek and Find: This model, released in 1997, was inspired by a church that once stood in Welaka, Florida.

Shave and a Haircut: Based on a 1900s barbershop in Wytopitloch, Maine, *Shave and a Haircut* was available in the USA beginning in 1993.

Simply Amish: Built c.1700, *Simply Amish* shows a typical barn used for storage. It is based on the buildings in the Amish community in Harrison County, Indiana.

16.9 Cents Per Gallon: The combination of a general store and filling station would have served the needs of the entire community in the early 20th century.

THE AMERICAN LANDMARKS COLLECTION by Ray Day

Small Town Library: Located in Rugby, Tennessee, this building was constructed in the late 1800s for the benefit of the community.

Spring Victorian: This distinctive house was constructed in the late 19th century in Georgetown, Colorado. The model was issued in 1994.

Victoriana: Inspired by houses in the coastal town of Rockport, Maine, this model of a 19th century house was introduced in June 1991 in a limited edition of 2,500.

Watson's Collectibles: This model produced in 1999 was a tribute to Winnie Watson, founder of the largest Collectibles exposition in America.

DISNEYANA™

Fire House 105™: The first model produced for Disney by Lilliput Lane, *Fire House 105* was limited to 501 pieces, which sold out in a day.

The Hall of Presidents™: Based on the building of the same name at the Walt Disney World Resort, Orlando, this model was released in a limited edition of 500.

The Haunted Mansion™: Released during a Disneyana event held September 2nd-6th, 1997, this model was produced in a limited edition of 500.

Main Street Cinema™: The 1999 convention piece, *Main Street Cinema* is a replica of the cinema at Walt Disney World Resort, Orlando, Florida.

COSY CORNER

Code No.:	Unknown
Size:	2 ¾″, 7.0 cm
Backstamp:	I-1
Introduced:	1990-1991
Series:	Collectors Club
Can.	$95.00
U.S.	$75.00
U.K.	£50.00

COTMAN COTTAGE
First Version - 4″

Code No.:	Unknown
Size:	4″, 10.1 cm
Backstamp:	L
Introduced:	1993-1993
Location:	Suffolk
Series:	Anniversary Editions
Can.	$225.00
U.S.	$165.00
U.K.	£100.00

COTMAN COTTAGE
Second Version - 1½″

Code No.:	Unknown
Size:	1 ½″, 3.9 cm
Backstamp:	None
Introduced:	1996-1996
Location:	Suffolk
Series:	Dream Cottage Miniatures
Can.	$40.00
U.S.	$25.00
U.K.	£15.00

Note: Free with purchase of £29.95.

Photograph not available at press time.

See previous image for shape outline.

COUNTING HOUSE CORNER
First Variation (Without plinth, grey windows)

Code No.:	Unknown
Size:	4 ½″, 11.9 cm
Backstamp:	M
Introduced:	1993 in a limited edition of 3,093
Series:	Special Editions
Can.	$1,350.00
U.S.	$ 950.00
U.K.	£ 550.00

COUNTING HOUSE CORNER
Second Variation (With plinth, black windows)

Code No.:	Unknown
Size:	4 ½″, 11.9 cm (not including plinth)
Backstamp:	M
Introduced:	1993 in a limited edition of 365
Series:	Special Editions
Can.	$1,100.00
U.S.	$ 750.00
U.K.	£ 500.00

COUNTRY CANVAS™

Code No.:	L2070
Size:	2 ½″, 6.4 cm
Backstamp:	P-2
Introduced:	1997-1999
Series:	Coca-Cola™ Collection
Can.	$40.00
U.S.	$25.00
U.K.	£15.00

COUNTRY CHURCH
Style One, First Variation
(Brown building, white bell tower)

Code No.:	Unknown
Size:	2 ¾", 7.0 cm
Backstamp:	C
Introduced:	1984-1984
Series:	American (1st)
Can.	$1,200.00
U.S.	$ 800.00
U.K.	£ 500.00

COUNTRY CHURCH
Style One, Second Variation
(White building, brown bell tower)

Code No.:	Unknown
Size:	2 ¾", 7.0 cm
Backstamp:	C
Introduced:	1984-1985
Series:	American (1st)
Can.	$1,000.00
U.S.	$ 700.00
U.K.	£ 450.00

Note: Of the 500 produced, the majority were in the second colourway.

COUNTRY CHURCH
Style Two

Code No.:	522
Size:	4", 10.1 cm
Backstamp:	H-1
Introduced:	1989-1992
Varieties:	One Nation Under God
Location:	Shelbyville, Indiana
Series:	American Landmarks
Can.	$140.00
U.S.	$100.00
U.K.	£ 65.00

"COUNTRY FRESH PICKINS"™

Code No.:	897
Size:	3 ½", 9.0 cm
Backstamp:	N-2
Introduced:	1995-1999
Location:	Indiana
Series:	Coca-Cola™ Country
Can.	$175.00
U.S.	$125.00
U.K.	£ 80.00

COUNTRY LIVING

Code No.:	L2171
Size:	5 ¼", 13.3 cm
Backstamp:	Q-2
Introduced:	1998 to the present
Series:	English
Can.	$480.00
U.S.	$275.00
U.K.	£125.00

COUNTRYSIDE BARN

Code No.:	524
Size:	3 ½", 8.9 cm
Backstamp:	H-1
Introduced:	1989-1992
Series:	American Landmarks
Can.	$125.00
U.S.	$ 80.00
U.K.	£ 50.00

COVERED BRIDGE

Code No.:	Unknown
Size:	2 ½", 6.4 cm
Backstamp:	C
Introduced:	1984-1985
Series:	American (1st)
Can.	$2,200.00
U.S.	$1,500.00
U.K.	£ 950.00

COVERED MEMORIES

Code No.:	533
Size:	3 ½", 8.9 cm
Backstamp:	I-1
Introduced:	1990-1993
Series:	American Landmarks
Can.	$200.00
U.S.	$150.00
U.K.	£ 95.00

COWSLIP COTTAGE

Code No.:	L2126
Size:	3", 7.6 cm
Backstamp:	Q-2
Introduced:	1998 to the present
Location:	Munslow, Shropshire
Series:	English
Can.	$150.00
U.S.	$120.00
U.K.	£ 39.95

CRADLE COTTAGE

Code No.:	009
Size:	4", 10.1 cm
Backstamp:	O-2
Introduced:	1996-1999
Location:	Sulham, Berkshire
Series:	English: South-East
Can.	$140.00
U.S.	$100.00
U.K.	£ 65.00

CRAIGIEVAR CASTLE

Code No.:	Unknown
Size:	6 ¾", 17.2 cm
Backstamp:	H-1
Introduced:	1989-1991
Location:	Aberdeen, Scotland
Series:	Scottish
Can.	$400.00
U.S.	$275.00
U.K.	£175.00

CRANBERRY COTTAGE

Code No.:	626
Size:	2 ½", 6.4 cm
Backstamp:	K-1
Introduced:	1992-1996
Varieties:	Ashberry Cottage
Location:	Cotswolds
Series:	Christmas
Can.	$50.00
U.S.	$35.00
U.K.	£20.00

Note: This model has no snow, and no South Bend backstamp/number 10.

CRATHIE CHURCH

Code No.:	L2084
Size :	4", 10.1 cm
Backstamp:	P-1
Introduced:	1997 to the present
Location:	Balmoral, Scotland
Series:	Scottish
Can.	$100.00
U.S.	$ 60.00
U.K.	£ 25.95

CREEL COTTAGE

Code No.:	694
Size:	2 ½", 6.4 cm
Backstamp:	M
Introduced:	1994-1997
Location:	Polperro, Cornwall
Series:	English: South-West
Can.	$45.00
U.S.	$30.00
U.K.	£20.00

CRENDON MANOR

Code No.:	Unknown
Size:	4 ½", 11.9 cm
Backstamp:	E
Introduced:	1986 in a limited edition of 1,500
Location:	Long Crendon, Buckinghamshire
Series:	Collectors Club
Can.	$1,300.00
U.S.	$ 900.00
U.K.	£ 575.00

CRISPIN COTTAGE

Code No.:	L2006
Size:	3", 7.6 cm
Backstamp:	0-2
Introduced:	1996-1999
Location:	Westmarsh, Kent
Series:	English: South-East
Can.	$60.00
U.S.	$45.00
U.K.	£30.00

CROFTER'S COTTAGE / THE CROFT

First Version
(Light grey, without sheep)

Code No.:	Unknown
Size:	2 ¼", 5.7 cm
Backstamp:	A-1, None
Introduced:	1982-1982
Series:	Scottish
Can.	$1,350.00
U.S.	$ 850.00
U.K.	£ 550.00

CROFTER'S COTTAGE / THE CROFT

Second Version
(Slate grey, without sheep)

Code No.:	Unknown
Size:	2 ¼", 5.7cm
Backstamp:	B
Introduced:	1982-1984
Series:	Scottish
Can.	$1,000.00
U.S.	$ 675.00
U.K.	£ 425.00

Note: Renamed "The Croft" in 1982.

CROFTER'S COTTAGE / THE CROFT

Third Version
(Very light grey, with sheep)

Code No.:	Unknown
Size:	2 ½", 6.4 cm
Backstamp:	C
Introduced:	1984-1991
Series:	Scottish
Can.	$65.00
U.S.	$50.00
U.K.	£30.00

Note: The chimney pots were removed.

CROWN INN

Code No.:	Unknown
Size:	4 ½", 11.9 cm
Backstamp:	G
Introduced:	1988-1992
Location:	Chiddingford, Surrey
Series:	English: South-East
Can.	$175.00
U.S.	$125.00
U.K.	£ 80.00

CRUCK END

Code No.:	855
Size:	3 ¾", 9.5 cm
Backstamp:	O-1
Introduced:	1996-1996
Location:	Didbrook, Gloucestershire
Series:	Anniversary Editions
Can.	$140.00
U.S.	$100.00
U.K.	£ 60.00

THE CUDDY

Code No.:	L2001
Size:	2 ½", 6.4 cm
Backstamp:	O-2
Introduced:	1996-1999
Location:	Chiswell, Dorset
Series:	English: South-West
Can.	$35.00
U.S.	$25.00
U.K.	£15.00

CULLODEN COTTAGE

Code No.:	486
Size:	2 ½", 6.4 cm
Backstamp:	H-1
Introduced:	1989-1998
Series:	Scottish
Can.	$45.00
U.S.	$30.00
U.K.	£20.00

CULROSS HOUSE

Code No.:	500
Size:	3", 7.6 cm
Backstamp:	K-1
Introduced:	1992-1997
Series:	Scottish
Can.	$90.00
U.S.	$60.00
U.K.	£40.00

CURLEW COTTAGE

Code No:	Unknown
Size:	3", 7.6 cm
Backstamp:	L
Introduced:	1993-1994
Location:	South Yorkshire
Series:	Collectors Club

Can.	$175.00
U.S.	$125.00
U.K.	£ 80.00

DAISY COTTAGE

Code No.:	439
Size:	2", 5.0 cm
Backstamp:	J
Introduced:	1991-1997
Location:	Hertfordshire
Series:	English: South-East

Can.	$45.00
U.S.	$30.00
U.K.	£20.00

DALE FARM

First Version, First Variation
(17 Windows, light colour)

Code No.:	Unknown
Size:	2 ¼", 5.7 cm
Backstamp:	A-1, None
Introduced:	1982-1982
Series:	English: Northern

Can.	$1,400.00
U.S.	$1,000.00
U.K.	£ 650.00

Photograph not available at press time.

See previous image for shape outline.

DALE FARM

First Version, Second Variation
(17 Windows, dark colour)

Code No.:	Unknown
Size:	2 ¼", 5.7 cm
Backstamp:	A-2
Introduced:	1982-1983
Series:	English: Northern

Can.	$1,000.00
U.S.	$ 750.00
U.K.	£ 475.00

DALE FARM

Second Version (15 Windows)

Code No.:	Unknown
Size:	2 ¼", 5.7 cm
Backstamp:	B
Introduced:	1983-1986
Series:	English: Northern

Can.	$900.00
U.S.	$600.00
U.K.	£475.00

Note: A bush was also added on the left side of the building.

DALE HEAD

Code No.:	Unknown
Size:	2 ¾", 7.0 cm
Backstamp:	E
Introduced:	1986-1988
Series:	English: Northern

Can.	$130.00
U.S.	$ 85.00
U.K.	£ 55.00

DALE HOUSE

First Version (Small windows, doorway)

Code No.:	Unknown
Size:	2 ½", 6 cm
Backstamp:	A-1, A-2, None
Introduced:	1982-1983
Series:	English: Northern
Can.	$1,400.00
U.S.	$1,000.00
U.K.	£ 650.00

DALE HOUSE

Second Version (Large windows, doorway, more foliage)

Code No.:	Unknown
Size:	2 ¾", 7.0 cm
Backstamp:	C
Introduced:	1983-1996
Series:	English: Northern
Can.	$1,100.00
U.S.	$ 800.00
U.K.	£ 500.00

Photograph not available at press time.

See previous image for shape outline.

THE DALESMAN

Code No.:	L2012
Size:	3 ¾", 9.5 cm
Backstamp:	O-2
Introduced:	1996-1999
Location:	North Yorkshire
Series:	English: Northern
Can.	$95.00
U.S.	$75.00
U.K.	£50.00

DAYDREAMS

Code No.:	L2146
Size:	3 ¼", 8.3 cm
Backstamp:	P-1
Introduced:	1997 to the present
Location:	Rush County, Indiana
Series:	An American Journey
Can.	N/A
U.S.	$75.00
U.K.	£35.95

DECK THE HALL™

Code No.:	150-3021
Size:	4 ¾", 12.1 cm
Backstamp:	R
Introduced:	1999-1999
Varieties:	The Hall of Presidents
Series:	Disneyana™
Can.	N/A
U.S.	$250.00
U.K.	N/A

Note: This is a reworking of the "Hall of Presidents", but with Christmas trees and decorations.

DEER PARK HALL

Code No.:	173
Size:	5 ¼", 13.3 cm
Backstamp:	G
Introduced:	1988-1989
Location:	East Sussex Downs
Series:	Christmas Specials
Can.	$200.00
U.S.	$150.00
U.K.	£ 95.00

DERWENT-LE-DALE

Code No.:	631
Size:	2 ¾", 7.0 cm
Backstamp:	K-1
Introduced:	1992-1998
Location:	Derwent-le-Dale
Series:	English: Northern
Can.	$75.00
U.S.	$50.00
U.K.	£30.00

DEVON LEIGH

Code No.:	L2091
Size:	3 ½", 8.9 cm
Backstamp:	P-1
Introduced:	1997-1999
Location:	Kingsbridge, Devon
Series:	English
Can.	$125.00
U.S.	$ 80.00
U.K.	£ 50.00

DIAL COTTAGE

First Version - 4 ½"

Code No.:	525
Size:	4 ½", 11.9 cm
Backstamp:	L
Introduced:	1990-1995
Location:	Bristol
Series:	1. English: South-West 2. Blaise Hamlet
Can.	$165.00
U.S.	$115.00
U.K.	£ 75.00

DIAL COTTAGE

Second Version - 2 ½"

Code No.:	525
Size:	2 ½", 6.4 cm
Backstamp:	L
Introduced:	1993-1995
Location:	Bristol
Series:	Classics
Can.	$100.00
U.S.	$ 75.00
U.K.	£ 50.00

DE DIAMANTAIR

Code No.:	123
Size:	5 ¾", 14.6 cm
Backstamp:	J
Introduced:	1991-1998
Variation:	Aan de Amstel
Location:	Amsterdam
Series:	Netherlands
Can.	$90.00
U.S.	$60.00
U.K.	£40.00

DIAMOND COTTAGE

Style One - 4 ¾"

Code No.:	Unknown
Size:	4 ¾", 12.1 cm
Backstamp:	H-1
Introduced:	1989-1993
Location:	Bristol
Series:	Blaise Hamlet
Can.	$165.00
U.S.	$115.00
U.K.	£ 70.00

Note: The roof on De Diamantair is grey, rather than white (Aan de Amstel).

DIAMOND COTTAGE

Style Two - 2 ½″

Code No.:	Unknown
Size:	2 ½″, 6.4 cm
Backstamp:	L
Introduced:	1993-1995
Location:	Bristol
Series:	Classics Collection
Can.	$100.00
U.S.	$ 75.00
U.K.	£ 50.00

DIXIE BOTTLING COMPANY™

Code No.:	L2265
Size:	3 ½″, 8.9 cm
Backstamp:	R
Introduced:	1999-2000
Series:	Coca-Cola™ Collection
Can.	N/A
U.S.	$160.00
U.K.	N/A

DOG DAYS OF SUMMER

Code No.:	L2151
Size:	2 ½″, 6.4 cm
Backstamp:	P-2
Introduced:	1997-2000
Location:	Kirbyville, Missouri
Series:	An American Journey
Can.	N/A
U.S.	$55.00
U.K.	£26.95

DONEGAL COTTAGE

First Variation (Dark Blue-Grey Windows, Slate Grey Pathway)

Code No.:	Unknown
Size:	2″, 5.0 cm
Backstamp:	F
Introduced:	1987-1989
Series:	Irish
Can.	$60.00
U.S.	$40.00
U.K.	£25.00

DONEGAL COTTAGE

Second Variation (Light Blue-Grey Windows, Buff Pathway)

Code No.:	Unknown
Size:	2″, 5.0 cm
Backstamp:	F
Introduced:	c.1989-1992
Series:	Irish
Can.	$60.00
U.S.	$40.00
U.K.	£25.00

DORMOUSE COTTAGE

Code No.:	L2038
Size:	3 ½″, 8.9 cm
Backstamp:	P-1
Introduced:	1997-1997
Location:	Inberrow, Worcs.
Series:	Special Editions
Can.	$90.00
U.S.	$60.00
U.K.	£40.00

Note: The original door was available in cream, but the customer could choose from a variety of colours.

DOUBLE COTTAGE
First Version - 5″

Code No.: 354
Size: 5″, 12.7 cm
Backstamp: J
Introduced: 1991-1996
Location: Bristol
Series: 1. Blaise Hamlet
2. English: South-West

Can. $195.00
U.S. $135.00
U.K. £ 85.00

DOUBLE COTTAGE
Second Version - 2 ½″

Code No.: Unknown
Size: 2 ½″, 6.4 cm
Backstamp: L
Introduced: 1993-1995
Location: Bristol
Series: Classics

Can. $100.00
U.S. $ 75.00
U.K. £ 50.00

DOVE COTTAGE
First Version (With name)

Code No.: Unknown
Size: 2 ½″, 6.4 cm
Backstamp: A-1
Introduced: 1983-1983
Location: Grasmere
Series: English: Northern

Can. $1,200.00
U.S. $ 850.00
U.K. £ 550.00

DOVE COTTAGE
Second Version (Without name)

Code No.: Unknown
Size: 2 ½″, 6.4 cm
Backstamp: B, C
Introduced: 1983-1988
Location: Grasmere
Series: English: Northern

Can. $135.00
U.S. $ 95.00
U.K. £ 60.00

DOVE COTTAGE - GRASMERE

Code No.: L2198
Size: 2 ¾″, 7.0 cm
Backstamp: Q-2
Introduced: 1998 to the present
Location: Grasmere
Series: Visitors Centre Exclusive

Can. N/A
U.S. $65.00
U.K. £26.95

Note: This was William Wordsworth's home 1799-1808.

THE DOVECOT

Code No.: Unknown
Size: 3″, 7.6 cm
Backstamp: H-1
Introduced: 1989-1990
Series: Collectors Club

Can. $120.00
U.S. $ 80.00
U.K. £ 50.00

DOVETAILS

Code No.:	609
Size:	3 ¼", 8.3 cm
Backstamp:	J
Introduced:	1991-1996
Location:	Ilkley, Yorkshire
Series:	English: Northern
Can.	$90.00
U.S.	$60.00
U.K.	£40.00

DRAPERS

First Version (With window to left side wall)

Code No.:	Unknown
Size:	2 ¾", 7.0 cm
Backstamp:	A-1
Introduced:	1982-1982
Location:	Lincoln
Series:	English: Midlands
Can.	$3,500.00
U.S.	$2,500.00
U.K.	£1,500.00

Note: Only 360 pieces were produced.

DRAPERS

Second Version (Without window to left side wall)

Code No.:	Unknown
Size:	2 ¾", 7.0 cm
Backstamp:	A-1
Introduced:	1982-1983
Location:	Lincoln
Series:	English: Midlands
Can.	$3,500.00
U.S.	$2,500.00
U.K.	£1,500.00

Note: Beige-yellow or red windows.

DUART CASTLE

Code No.:	373
Size:	5", 12.7 cm
Backstamp:	K-1
Introduced:	1992 in a limited edition of 3,000
Location:	Isle of Mull
Series:	Scottish
Can.	$550.00
U.S.	$400.00
U.K.	£250.00

DUCKDOWN COTTAGE

Code No.:	775
Size:	3 ½", 8.9 cm
Backstamp:	N-1
Introduced:	1995-1997
Location:	Ramsbury, Wiltshire
Series:	English: South-West
Can.	$90.00
U.S.	$60.00
U.K.	£40.00

EAMONT LODGE

Code No.:	640
Size:	4 ¼", 10.8 cm
Backstamp:	L
Introduced:	1993-1993
Location:	Penrith, Cumbria
Series:	Christmas Lodge
Can.	$200.00
U.S.	$145.00
U.K.	£ 90.00

EAST NEUK

Code No.:	Unknown
Size:	2", 5.0 cm
Backstamp:	F
Introduced:	1987-1991
Series:	Scottish
Can.	$60.00
U.S.	$40.00
U.K.	£25.00

EDINBURGH CASTLE

Code No.:	L2247
Size:	3 ½", 8.9 cm
Backstamp:	R
Introduced:	1999 to the present
Location:	Edinburgh
Series:	Britain's Heritage™: Royal Residences
Can.	$160.00
U.S.	$110.00
U.K.	£ 39.95

EDZELL SUMMER-HOUSE

Code No.:	650
Size:	4", 10.1 cm
Backstamp:	L
Introduced:	1993-1997
Location:	Near Brechin
Series:	Scottish
Can.	$100.00
U.S.	$ 70.00
U.K.	£ 45.00

EILEAN DONAN CASTLE

Code No.:	491
Size:	5", 12.7 cm
Backstamp:	H-1
Introduced:	1990-1999
Series:	Scottish
Can.	$225.00
U.S.	$160.00
U.K.	£100.00

ELM COTTAGE

Code No.:	691
Size:	2 ¾", 7.0 cm
Backstamp:	M
Introduced:	1994-1997
Location:	Chippenham, Wiltshire
Series:	English: Midlands
Can.	$60.00
U.S.	$40.00
U.K.	£25.00

ERISKAY CROFT

Code No.:	499
Size:	2 ¼", 5.7 cm
Backstamp:	K-1
Introduced:	1992-1999
Location:	Hebrides
Series:	Scottish
Can.	$50.00
U.S.	$35.00
U.K.	£20.00

EROS

Code No.:	L2290
Size:	5", 12.7 cm
Backstamp:	R
Introduced:	1999 to the present
Location:	London
Series:	Britains Heritage™
Can.	N/A
U.S.	$60.00
U.K.	£25.95

ESSEX COTTAGE

Code No.:	Unknown
Size:	3", 7.6 cm
Backstamp:	L
Introduced:	1993-1994
Series:	Paint Your Own
Can.	$425.00
U.S.	$300.00
U.K.	£190.00

Note: Prices refer to unpainted models, which are more valuable.

EVERGREENS

Code No.:	L2061
Size:	2 ¾", 7.0 cm
Backstamp:	P-1
Introduced:	1997-1997
Location:	The Shambles, York
Series:	Christmas Annual Ornament
Can.	$45.00
U.S.	$30.00
U.K.	£20.00

FALLS MILL

Code No.:	525
Size:	4 ¾", 12.1 cm
Backstamp:	H-1
Introduced:	1989-1992
Location:	Belvedere, Tennessee
Series:	American Landmarks
Can.	$225.00
U.S.	$150.00
U.K.	£100.00

DER FAMILIENSCHREIN

Code No.:	Unknown
Size:	4", 10.1 cm
Backstamp:	G
Introduced:	1988-1991
Series:	German
Can.	$140.00
U.S.	$100.00
U.K.	£ 65.00

FARRIERS

Code No.:	Unknown
Size:	2 ½", 6.4 cm
Backstamp:	D
Introduced:	1985-1990
Location:	Worcestershire
Series:	English: Midlands
Can.	$100.00
U.S.	$ 75.00
U.K.	£ 50.00

FARTHING LODGE

Code No.:	436
Size:	2 ½", 6.4 cm
Backstamp:	J
Introduced:	1991-1996
Series:	English: Midlands
Can.	$45.00
U.S.	$30.00
U.K.	£20.00

FIDDLER'S FOLLY

Code No.:	L2004
Size:	2 ½", 6.4 cm
Backstamp:	O-2
Introduced:	1996-1999
Location:	Pershore, Worcestershire
Series:	English: Midlands
Can.	$45.00
U.S.	$30.00
U.K.	£20.00

FILL 'ER UP AND CHECK THE OIL™

Code No.:	896
Size:	3", 7.6 cm
Backstamp:	N-2
Introduced:	1995-1999
Series:	Coca-Cola™ Country
Can.	$140.00
U.S.	$ 90.00
U.K.	£ 60.00

Note: All pieces in the series are hand-numbered and exclusive to North America.

FINCHINGFIELDS

Code No.:	636
Size:	3 ½", 8.9 cm
Backstamp:	K-1
Introduced:	1992-1995
Location:	Finchingfields, Essex
Series:	English: South-East
Can.	$100.00
U.S.	$ 75.00
U.K.	£ 50.00

FINDERS KEEPERS

Code No.:	L2296
Size:	2 ½", 6.4 cm
Backstamp:	R
Introduced:	1999-1999
Series:	Special Edition
Can.	$75.00
U.S.	$50.00
U.K.	£30.00

Note: Available when £29.95/$75.00 U.S. was spent on Lilliput Lane Cottages.

FIR TREE COTTAGE

Code No.:	848
Size:	2 ¾", 7.0 cm
Backstamp:	O-2
Introduced:	1996-1996
Location:	Grasmere, Cumbria
Series:	Christmas Annual Ornament
Can.	$35.00
U.S.	$25.00
U.K.	£15.00

FIRE HOUSE 1

Code No.:	556
Size:	4 ¼", 10.8 cm
Backstamp:	J
Introduced:	1991-1997
Location:	Maine
Series:	American Landmarks
Can.	$90.00
U.S.	$65.00
U.K.	£45.00

FIRE HOUSE 105™

Code No.:	Unknown
Size:	4 ½", 11.9 cm
Backstamp:	Special limited edition Disney Stamp
Introduced:	1995 in a limited edition of 501
Location:	Disneyland, Anaheim, California
Series:	Disneyana™
Can.	$1,000.00
U.S.	$ 700.00
U.K.	£ 450.00

THE FIRST NOEL

Code No.:	L2239
Size:	4", 10.1 cm
Backstamp:	R
Introduced:	1999-1999
Series:	Christmas Special
Can.	$175.00
U.S.	$125.00
U.K.	£ 80.00

FIRST SNOW AT BLUEBELL

Code No.:	L2022
Size:	4", 10.1 cm
Backstamp:	Unknown
Introduced:	1997 in a limited edition of 3,500
Varieties:	Bluebell Farm
Series:	English
Can.	$325.00
U.S.	$225.00
U.K.	£150.00

FISHERMAN'S BOTHY

Code No.:	489
Size:	2", 5.0 cm
Backstamp:	H-1
Introduced:	1990-1999
Series:	Scottish
Can.	$55.00
U.S.	$35.00
U.K.	£20.00

FISHERMAN'S COTTAGE

Code No.:	Unknown
Size:	2", 5.0 cm
Backstamp:	D
Introduced:	1985-1989
Location:	Boscastie, Cornwall
Series:	English: South-West
Can.	$100.00
U.S.	$ 75.00
U.K.	£ 50.00

FIVEWAYS

Code No.:	043
Size:	2 ¾", 7.0 cm
Backstamp:	H-1
Introduced:	1989-1995
Series:	English: Midlands
Can.	$65.00
U.S.	$50.00
U.K.	£30.00

FLATFORD LOCK

Code No.:	L2232
Size:	4", 10.1 cm
Backstamp:	R
Introduced:	1999 to the present
Series:	English
Can.	$450.00
U.S.	$275.00
U.K.	£125.00

FLAXTON BECK

Code No.:	Unknown
Size:	2 ¾", 7.0 cm
Backstamp:	L
Introduced:	1993-1994
Series:	Paint Your Own
Can.	$140.00
U.S.	$100.00
U.K.	£ 65.00

Note: Prices refer to unpainted models, which are more valuable.

FLOWERPOTS

Code No.:	L2009
Size:	3 ½", 8.9 cm
Backstamp:	O-2
Introduced:	1996-1999
Location:	Kent
Series:	English: South-East
Can.	$60.00
U.S.	$45.00
U.K.	£30.00

FLOWER SELLERS

Code No.:	600
Size:	4", 10.1 cm
Backstamp:	J
Introduced:	1991-1996
Location:	London
Series:	English: South-East
Can.	$100.00
U.S.	$ 75.00
U.K.	£ 50.00

FORGE BARN

Code No.:	Unknown
Size:	2 ½", 6.4 cm
Backstamp:	B
Introduced:	1984-1985
Series:	American (1st)
Can.	$900.00
U.S.	$600.00
U.K.	£375.00

Note: Only 275 models were produced.

FORGET-ME-NOT

Code No.: Unknown
Size: 3 ¼″, 8.3 cm
Backstamp: K-1
Introduced: 1992-1993
Series: Collectors Club

Can. $175.00
U.S. $130.00
U.K. £ 85.00

FOUNTAINS ABBEY

Code No.: Unknown
Size: 6″, 15.2 cm
Backstamp: Special Limited Edition
Introduced: 1995 in a limited edition of 3,500
Location: Yorkshire
Series: Studley Royal

Can. $500.00
U.S. $350.00
U.K. £225.00

FOUR SEASONS

Code No.: 061
Size: 4″, 10.1 cm
Backstamp: F
Introduced: 1987-1991
Location: Warwickshire
Series: English: Midlands

Can. $125.00
U.S. $ 85.00
U.K. £ 50.00

FOURTH OF JULY

Code No.: L2163
Size: 3″, 7.6 cm
Backstamp: Unknown
Introduced: 1998 in a limited edition of 1,776
Location: Bellville, Ohio
Series: Allegiance

Can. $100.00
U.S. $ 75.00
U.K. £ 45.00

FOXGLOVE FIELDS

Code No.: 151
Size: 3 ¼″, 8.3 cm
Backstamp: L
Introduced: 1993-1997
Location: Credenhill, Herefordshire
Series: English: Midlands

Can. $100.00
U.S. $ 75.00
U.K. £ 50.00

FRAGRANT HAVEN

Code No.: L2197
Size: 4″, 10.1 cm
Backstamp: Q-2
Introduced: 1998 to the present
Series: Secret Gardens™

Can. $150.00
U.S. $ 90.00
U.K. £ 39.95

FREE RANGE

Code No.:	L2181
Size:	2 ¼", 5.7 cm
Backstamp:	Q-2
Introduced:	1998-2000
Series:	English
Can.	$60.00
U.S.	$35.00
U.K.	£15.50

FRESH BREAD

Code No.:	683
Size:	3 ½", 8.9 cm
Backstamp:	M
Introduced:	1994-1999
Location:	Silver Plume, Colorado
Series:	American Landmarks
Can.	$140.00
U.S.	$100.00
U.K.	£ 65.00

FRESH TODAY

Code No.:	L2256
Size:	3", 7.6 cm
Backstamp:	R
Introduced:	1999-2000
Series:	Collectors Club
Can.	N/A
U.S.	$70.00
U.K.	£17.50

FROSTY MORNING

Code No.:	L2128
Size:	4 ¼", 10.8 cm
Backstamp:	Q-2
Introduced:	1998-1998
Series:	Christmas Specials
Can.	$175.00
U.S.	$125.00
U.K.	£ 80.00

FRUITS OF EDEN

Code No.:	L2250
Size:	5 ¼", 13.3 cm
Backstamp:	R
Introduced:	1999 to the present
Series:	Secret Gardens™
Can.	$140.00
U.S.	$ 80.00
U.K.	£ 35.95

FRY DAYS

Code No.:	L2023
Size:	3 ¾", 9.5 cm
Backstamp:	O-2
Introduced:	1996-2000
Location:	Kendal, Cumbria
Series:	English: Northern
Can.	$120.00
U.S.	$ 70.00
U.K.	£ 35.95

FUCHSIA COTTAGE

Code No.:	001
Size:	2 ¼", 5.7 cm
Backstamp:	O-1
Introduced:	1996-1999
Location:	Corfe, Dorest
Series:	English: South-West
Can.	$45.00
U.S.	$30.00
U.K.	£20.00

THE GABLES

Code No.:	Unknown
Size:	5 ¼", 13.3 cm
Backstamp:	F
Introduced:	1987-1992
Series:	English: South-East
Can.	$250.00
U.S.	$175.00
U.K.	£125.00

GAMEKEEPER'S COTTAGE

First Variation (Red roof; South Bend 1991 backstamp)

Code No.:	Unknown
Size:	3 ½", 8.9 cm
Backstamp:	J
Introduced:	1991 in a special edition of 350
Location:	Ragley Hall, Warwickshire
Series:	Special Editions
Can.	$500.00
U.S.	$350.00
U.K.	£225.00

GAMEKEEPER'S COTTAGE

Second Variation (Sienna roof; Lilliput Lane backstamp)

Code No.:	Unknown
Size:	3 ½", 8.9 cm
Backstamp:	J
Introduced:	1991-1992
Location:	Ragley Hall, Warwickshire
Series:	Special Editions
Can.	$140.00
U.S.	$100.00
U.K.	£ 65.00

GARDENER'S COTTAGE

Code No.:	Unknown
Size:	3 ¾", 9.5 cm
Backstamp:	J
Introduced:	1991-1992
Series:	Collectors Club
Can.	$225.00
U.S.	$150.00
U.K.	£100.00

DAS GEBIRGSKIRCHLEIN

Code No.:	253
Size:	5", 12.7 cm
Backstamp:	F
Introduced:	1987-1998
Series:	German
Can.	$140.00
U.S.	$100.00
U.K.	£ 65.00

GENERAL STORE

First Version (Diagonal red lettering)

Code No.:	Unknown
Size:	2 ¾", 7.0 cm
Backstamp:	C
Introduced:	1984-Unknown
Series:	American (1st)
Can.	$1,400.00
U.S.	$1,000.00
U.K.	£ 650.00

Note: Approximately 50 of the 150 pieces produced are first version models.

GENERAL STORE

Second Version (Horizontal White Lettering)

Code No.:	Unknown
Size:	2 ¾", 7.0 cm
Backstamp:	C
Introduced:	Unknown-1985
Series:	American (1st)
Can.	$800.00
U.S.	$575.00
U.K.	£375.00

THE GEORGE INN

Code No.:	L2098
Size:	4", 10.1 cm
Backstamp:	Unknown
Introduced:	1997-2000
Location:	Somerset
Series:	English
Can.	N/A
U.S.	$225.00
U.K.	£ 99.95

Photograph not available at press time.

See next image for shape outline.

GERTRUDE'S GARDEN

Code No.:	767
Size:	3 ¾", 9.5 cm
Backstamp:	N-1
Introduced:	1995-1995
Location:	Badminton
Series:	Anniversary Editions
Can.	$225.00
U.S.	$160.00
U.K.	£100.00

GINGER AND PICKLES SHOP™

Code No.:	L2268
Size:	3 ½", 8.9 cm
Backstamp:	R
Introduced:	1999 to the present
Series:	Beatrix Potter™
Can.	N/A
U.S.	$53.00
U.K.	£25.95

THE GINGERBREAD SHOP

Code No.:	642
Size:	2 ½", 6.4 cm
Backstamp:	L
Introduced:	1993-1997
Series:	Christmas
Can.	$45.00
U.S.	$30.00
U.K.	£20.00

GLAMIS CASTLE

Code No.:	L2314
Size:	4 ¼", 10.8 cm
Backstamp:	R
Introduced:	2000-2000
Series:	Britains Heritage™

Can.	$300.00
U.S.	$275.00
U.K.	£ 85.95

GLENLOCHIE LODGE

Code No.:	493
Size:	4 ¾", 12.1 cm
Backstamp:	H-1
Introduced:	1990-1993
Series:	Scottish

Can.	$200.00
U.S.	$150.00
U.K.	£ 95.00

GOLD MINER'S CLAIM

First Version (Without snow)

Code No.:	629A
Size:	3 ¼", 8.3 cm
Backstamp:	K-1
Introduced:	1992-1992
Series:	American Landmarks

Can.	$1,250.00
U.S.	$ 900.00
U.K.	£ 575.00

Note: Approximately 15 pieces were released from the factory without snow.

GOLD MINER'S CLAIM

Second Version (With snow)

Code No.:	629B
Size:	3 ¼", 8.3 cm
Backstamp:	K-1
Introduced:	1992-1997
Series:	American Landmarks

Can.	$100.00
U.S.	$ 75.00
U.K.	£ 50.00

GOLDEN MEMORIES

Code No.:	L2139
Size:	3 ¾", 9.5 cm
Backstamp:	Q-2
Introduced:	1998-1999
Location:	Barthomley, Cheshire
Series:	English

Can.	$100.00
U.S.	$ 75.00
U.K.	£ 50.00

GOLDEN YEARS

Code No.:	L2048
Size:	2 ½", 6.4 cm
Backstamp:	P-1
Introduced:	1997 to the present
Location:	East Anglia
Series:	English

Can.	$40.00
U.S.	$25.00
U.K.	£ 9.95

THE GOOD LIFE

Code No.: L2237
Size: 4", 10.1 cm
Backstamp: R
Introduced: 1999-2000
Series: Collectors Club

Can. $200.00
U.S. $150.00
U.K. £ 55.00

GOSSIP GATE

Code No.: 010
Size: 4", 10.1 cm
Backstamp: O-1
Introduced: 1996-1999
Location: Lansing Village, Sussex
Series: English: South-East

Can. $200.00
U.S. $150.00
U.K. £ 95.00

GRANDMA AND GRANDPA'S

Code No.: L2321
Size: 2", 5.0 cm
Backstamp: R
Introduced: 2000 to the present
Series: English

Can. $50.00
U.S. $30.00
U.K. £13.50

GRANDMA BATTY'S TEA ROOM

Code No.: 774
Size: 3 ¾", 9.5 cm
Backstamp: N-1
Introduced: 1995-1998
Location: York
Series: English Tea Rooms

Can. $125.00
U.S. $ 80.00
U.K. £ 50.00

GRANNY SMITHS

Code No.: 614
Size: 2 ¾", 7.0 cm
Backstamp: K-1
Introduced: 1992-1996
Location: Worcestershire
Series: English: Midlands

Can. $50.00
U.S. $35.00
U.K. £20.00

GRANNY'S BONNET

Code No.: L2080
Size: 2 ¼", 5.7 cm
Backstamp: P-1
Introduced: 1997 to the present
Location: Buckinghamshire
Series: English

Can. $40.00
U.S. $25.00
U.K. £ 9.95

GRANTCHESTER MEADOWS

Code No.:	633
Size:	4″, 10.1 cm
Backstamp:	K-1
Introduced:	1992-1996
Location:	Cambridgeshire
Series:	English: South-East
Can.	$250.00
U.S.	$175.00
U.K.	£110.00

THE GREAT EQUATORIAL

Code No.:	L2242
Size:	5″, 12.7 cm
Backstamp:	R
Introduced:	1999-2000
Series:	Millennium
Can.	$160.00
U.S.	$ 90.00
U.K.	£ 39.95

GREAT EXPECTATIONS

Code No.:	L2129
Size:	2 ½″, 6.4 cm
Backstamp:	Q-2
Introduced:	1998-1998
Location:	Grassington, Yorkshire
Series:	Christmas Annual Ornament
Can.	$45.00
U.S.	$30.00
U.K.	£20.00

GREAT POINT LIGHT

First Variation (Brown windows/ housing)

Code No.:	534
Size:	4″, 10.1 cm
Backstamp:	I-2
Introduced:	1990-1990
Series:	American Landmarks
Can.	$140.00
U.S.	$100.00
U.K.	£ 60.00

Note: Approx. 500-800 pieces were produced in this colour variation.

GREAT POINT LIGHT

Second Variation (Blue windows/ housing)

Code No.:	534
Size:	4″, 10.1 cm
Backstamp:	I-2
Introduced:	1990-1999
Series:	American Landmarks
Can.	$65.00
U.S.	$45.00
U.K.	£30.00

GREAT WISHFORD

Code No.:	L2202
Size:	3 ¾″, 9.5 cm
Backstamp:	R
Introduced:	1999-1999
Series:	Helen Allingham
Can.	$160.00
U.S.	$ 70.00
U.K.	£ 30.00

GREEN GABLES

Code No.:	L2205
Size:	4 ¾", 12.0 cm
Backstamp:	P-1
Introduced:	1997 to the present
Location:	Wiveliscombe, Somerset
Series:	English
Can.	$350.00
U.S.	$225.00
U.K.	£ 99.95

THE GREENGROCER'S

Code No.:	622
Size:	3 ¾", 9.5 cm
Backstamp:	J
Introduced:	1991-1998
Location:	Cotswolds
Series:	Village Shops
Can.	$100.00
U.S.	$ 70.00
U.K.	£ 45.00

GREENSTED CHURCH

Code No.:	320
Size:	4", 10.1 cm
Backstamp:	H-1
Introduced:	1989-1995
Location:	Essex
Series:	English: South-East
Can.	$135.00
U.S.	$ 95.00
U.K.	£ 65.00

GRIST MILL

Code No.:	Unknown
Size:	2 ½", 6.4 cm
Backstamp:	C
Introduced:	1984-1985
Series:	American (1st)
Can.	$1,000.00
U.S.	$ 675.00
U.K.	£ 425.00

Note: Only 150 models were produced.

GUILDHALL

Code No.:	Unknown
Size:	5", 12.7 cm
Backstamp:	F
Introduced:	1987-1989
Location:	Thaxted, Essex
Series:	Special Editions
Can.	$350.00
U.S.	$250.00
U.K.	£165.00

GULLS CRY

Code No.:	L2182
Size:	2 ¼", 5.7 cm
Backstamp:	Q-2
Introduced:	1998 to the present
Series:	English
Can.	$60.00
U.S.	$35.00
U.K.	£15.50

GYPSY COTTAGE

Code No.:	L2282
Size:	3 ¼", 8.3 cm
Backstamp:	Unknown
Introduced:	1998
Series:	Paint Your Own
Can.	N/A
U.S.	$22.50
U.K.	£ 8.50

Note: Prices refer to unpainted models, which are more valuable.

HABERDASHERY

Code No.:	L2053
Size:	4", 10.1 cm
Backstamp:	P-1
Introduced:	1997-1999
Series:	Victorian Shops
Can.	$140.00
U.S.	$ 80.00
U.K.	£ 45.00

HADLEIGH COTTAGE

Code No.:	L2221
Size:	3 ½", 8.9 cm
Backstamp:	Q-2
Introduced:	1998 in a limited edition of 5,000
Series:	Special Edition
Can.	$130.00
U.S.	$100.00
U.K.	£ 45.00

HALCYON DAYS

Code No.:	L2047
Size:	4 ¼", 10.8 cm
Backstamp:	P-1
Introduced:	1997-1999
Location:	Stagsden, Bedfordshire
Series:	English
Can.	$200.00
U.S.	$150.00
U.K.	£ 65.00

THE HALL OF PRESIDENTS™

Code No.:	Unknown
Size:	4 ¾", 12.1 cm
Backstamp:	O-2
Introduced:	1996 in a limited edition of 500
Varieties:	Deck the Hall
Location:	Disneyworld, Florida
Series:	Disneyana™
Can.	$850.00
U.S.	$575.00
U.K.	£375.00

HAMPTON COURT PALACE

Code No.:	L2248
Size:	3 ½", 8.9 cm
Backstamp:	R
Introduced:	1999 to the present
Series:	Britain's Heritage™: Royal Residences
Can.	$100.00
U.S.	$ 60.00
U.K.	£ 25.95

HAMPTON MANOR

Code No.: L2056
Size: 4", 10.1 cm
Backstamp: P-1
Introduced: 1997-1998
Location: Lower Brockhampton, Herefordshire
Series: Collectors Club

Can. $125.00
U.S. $ 90.00
U.K. £ 60.00

HAMPTON MOAT

Code No.: L2057
Size: 2 ½", 6.4 cm
Backstamp: P-1
Introduced: 1997-1998
Location: Lower Brockhampton, Herefordshire
Series: Collectors Club

Can. $60.00
U.S. $40.00
U.K. £25.00

HAREBELL COTTAGE

Code No.: L2180
Size: 2 ½", 6.4 cm
Backstamp: Q-2
Introduction: 1998 to the present
Series: English

Can. $65.00
U.S. $35.00
U.K. £17.50

HARRIET'S COTTAGE

Code No.: L2018
Size: 3 ½", 8.95 cm
Backstamp: O-2
Introduced: 1996-1999
Location: Lyndhurst, Hampshire
Series: English: South-West

Can. $100.00
U.S. $ 75.00
U.K. £ 50.00

HARVEST HOME

Code No.: L2102
Size: 5", 12.7 cm
Backstamp: Unknown
Introduced: 1997 in a limited edition of 4,950
Location: Bearsted, Kent
Series: English

Can. $325.00
U.S. $225.00
U.K. £150.00

HARVEST MILL

Code No.: 654
Size: 4 ¼", 11.0 cm
Backstamp: M
Introduced: 1994 in a limited edition of 3,500
Location: Pigeon Forge, Tennessee
Series: American Landmarks

Can. $500.00
U.S. $350.00
U.K. £225.00

THE HAUNTED MANSION™

Code No.: Unknown
Size: 5″, 12.7 cm
Backstamp: P-1
Introduced: 1997 in a limited edition of 500
Series: Disneyana™

Can. $800.00
U.S. $550.00
U.K. £350.00

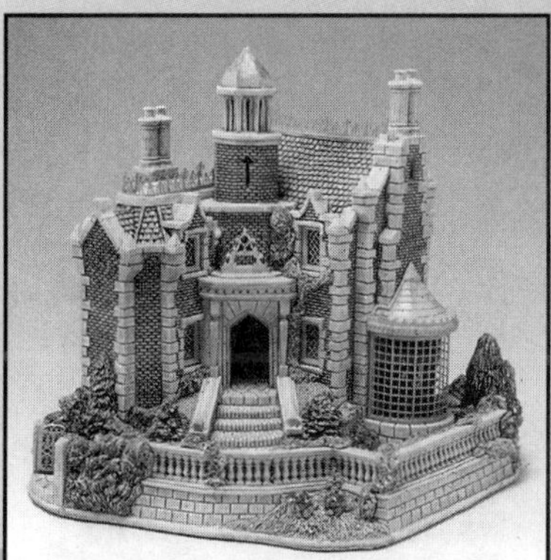

HAUS IM RHEINLAND

Code No.: 257
Size: 7″, 17.8 cm
Backstamp: F
Introduced: 1987-1998
Series: German

Can. $250.00
U.S. $175.00
U.K. £120.00

HAZARDS OF THE ROAD™

Code No.: 893
Size: 3 ¾″, 9.5 cm
Backstamp: N-2
Introduced: 1995-1999
Series: Coca-Cola™ Country

Can. $65.00
U.S. $50.00
U.K. £30.00

Note: Hand-numbered and made of resin, this model was exclusive to North America.

HEAVEN LEA COTTAGE

Code No.: Unknown
Size: 3 ¼″, 8.3 cm
Backstamp: L
Introduced: 1993-1994
Series: Collectors Club

Can. $200.00
U.S. $150.00
U.K. £100.00

HEBRIDEAN HAME

Code No.: Unknown
Size: 2 ½″, 6.4 cm
Backstamp: H-1
Introduced: 1990-1992
Location: Outer Hebrides
Series: Scottish

Can. $95.00
U.S. $65.00
U.K. £40.00

HEGARTY'S HOME

First Variation (Beige windows, white walls)

Code No.: Unknown
Size: 2″, 5.0 cm
Backstamp: H-1
Introduced: 1989-1990
Location: County Donegal
Series: Irish

Can. $200.00
U.S. $150.00
U.K. £ 95.00

HEGARTY'S HOME

Second Variation (Black windows, buff walls)

Code No.: Unknown
Size: 2", 5.0 cm
Backstamp: J
Introduced: 1990-1992
Location: County Donegal
Series: Irish

Can. $120.00
U.S. $ 80.00
U.K. £ 50.00

HELMERE COTTAGE

Code No.: 562
Size: 3 ¼", 8.3 cm
Backstamp: H-1
Introduced: 1989-1995
Location: Lakeland Fells
Series: English: Northern

Can. $95.00
U.S. $70.00
U.K. £45.00

HERMITAGE

First Version (Without lean-to)

Code No.: Unknown
Size: 2 ¼", 5.7 cm
Backstamp: D
Introduced: 1985-1986
Series: English

Can. $350.00
U.S. $250.00
U.K. £165.00

HERMITAGE

Second Version (With lean-to)

Code No.: Unknown
Size: 2 ½", 6.4 cm
Backstamp: E
Introduced: 1986-1990
Series: English

Can. $80.00
U.S. $55.00
U.K. £35.00

HESTERCOMBE GARDENS

Code No.: L2063
Size: 4 ½", 11.9 cm
Backstamp: Unknown
Introduced: 1997 in a limited edition of 3,950
Location: Hestercombe House, Somerset
Series: Garden

Can. $425.00
U.S. $300.00
U.K. £185.00

THE HIDEAWAY

Code No.: L2172
Size: 3 ½", 8.9 cm
Backstamp: Q-2
Introduced: 1998-2000
Series: English

Can. N/A
U.S. $120.00
U.K. £ 45.95

HIGH GHYLL FARM

Code No.: 635
Size: 5″, 12.7 cm
Backstamp: K-1
Introduced: 1992-1998
Varieties: Winter at High Ghyll
Location: Cumbria
Series: English: Northern

Can. $325.00
U.S. $225.00
U.K. £150.00

HIGH SPIRITS

Code No.: L2278
Size: 4″, 10.1 cm
Backstamp: R
Introduced: 1999 to the present
Series: English

Can. N/A
U.S. $85.00
U.K. £35.95

HIGHLAND LODGE

Code No.: Unknown
Size: 5 ¼″, 13.3 cm
Backstamp: K-1
Introduced: 1992-1992
Location: Kinloch Laggan
Series: Christmas Lodge

Can. $275.00
U.S. $195.00
U.K. £125.00

HILLTOP™

Code No.: L2273
Size: 3 ¼″, 8.3 cm
Backstamp: R
Introduced: 1999 to the present
Series: Beatrix Potter™

Can. N/A
U.S. $120.00
U.K. £ 49.95

HOLLANDSE POLDERMOLEN (DUTCH WINDMILL)

Code No.: L2306
Size: 5 ¾″, 14.6 cm
Backstamp: R
Introduced: 1999 to the present
Series: Dutch Heritage

Can. N/A
U.S. $65.00
U.K. £39.95

HOLLY COTTAGE

First Version (Tall chimney, thick base, duller colour)

Code No.: Unknown
Size: 3 ½″, 8.9 cm
Backstamp: A-1, A-2
Introduced: 1982-1984
Location: Cumbria
Series: English: Northern

Can. $700.00
U.S. $475.00
U.K. £350.00

HOLLY COTTAGE

Second Version (Short chimney, thin base, brighter colour)

Code No.:	Unknown
Size:	3 ¼", 8.3 cm
Backstamp:	C
Introduced:	1984-1988
Location:	Cumbria
Series:	English: Northern
Can.	$125.00
U.S.	$ 85.00
U.K.	£ 55.00

HOLLYTREE HOUSE

Code No.:	624
Size:	2 ½", 6.4 cm
Backstamp:	K-1
Introduced:	1992-1996
Series:	Christmas
Can.	$45.00
U.S.	$30.00
U.K.	£20.00

HOLME DYKE

Code No.:	Unknown
Size:	2 ½", 6.4 cm
Backstamp:	F
Introduced:	1987-1990
Location:	York
Series:	English: Northern
Can.	$90.00
U.S.	$65.00
U.K.	£40.00

HOLY NIGHT

Code No.:	682
Size:	4 ½", 11.9 cm
Backstamp:	M
Introduced:	1994-1999
Location:	Louisville, Kentucky
Series:	American Landmarks
Can.	$225.00
U.S.	$165.00
U.K.	£125.00

HOME FOR THE HOLIDAYS

Code No.:	519
Size:	4", 10.1 cm
Backstamp:	Ltd. Ed.
Introduced:	1996 in a limited edition of 2,596
Series:	American Landmarks
Can.	$650.00
U.S.	$450.00
U.K.	£275.00

HOME IS WHERE THE HEART IS

Code No.:	L2329
Size:	2 ¾", 7.0 cm
Backstamp:	R
Introduced:	2000 to the present
Series:	English
Can.	$70.00
U.S.	$50.00
U.K.	£19.95

HOME OF THE BRAVE

Code No.:	L2076
Size:	3 ¼", 8.3 cm
Backstamp:	O-2
Introduced:	1997-1999
Series:	Allegiance
Can.	$90.00
U.S.	$65.00
U.K.	£40.00

HOME SWEET HOME

Code No.:	558
Size:	3 ¼", 8.3 cm
Backstamp:	Unknown
Introduced:	1992-1998
Series:	American Landmarks
Can.	$125.00
U.S.	$ 85.00
U.K.	£ 55.00

HOMETOWN DEPOT

Code No.:	Unknown
Size:	3", 7.6 cm
Backstamp:	I-1
Introduced:	1990-1993
Location:	New Albany, Indiana
Series:	American Landmarks
Can.	$125.00
U.S.	$ 85.00
U.K.	£ 55.00

HONEY POT COTTAGE

Code No.:	863
Size:	3 ¾", 9.5 cm
Backstamp:	O-1
Introduced:	1996-1999
Location:	Finchingfield, Essex
Series:	English: South-East
Can.	$75.00
U.S.	$50.00
U.K.	£30.00

HONEYSUCKLE COTTAGE

Style One, First Version
(No bricks around base)

Code No.:	Unknown
Size:	3", 7.6 cm
Backstamp:	A-1
Introduced:	1982-1982
Location:	Oakhanger, Hampshire
Series:	English: South-East
Can.	$1,000.00
U.S.	$ 700.00
U.K.	£ 450.00

HONEYSUCKLE COTTAGE

Style One, Second Version
(One row of brick around base)

Code No.:	Unknown
Size:	3" , 7.6 cm
Backstamp:	A-2
Introduced:	1982-1983
Location:	Oakhanger, Hampshire
Series:	English: South-East
Can.	$675.00
U.S.	$475.00
U.K.	£300.00

Note: Many colour variations exist.

HONEYSUCKLE COTTAGE

Style One, Third Version
(Two rows of brick around base)

Code No.:	Unknown
Size:	3" , 7.6 cm
Backstamp:	C
Introduced:	1983-1987
Location:	Oakhanger, Hampshire
Series:	English: South-East
Can.	$175.00
U.S.	$130.00
U.K.	£100.00

Photograph not available at press time.

See previous page for shape outline.

HONEYSUCKLE COTTAGE 1992

Style Two

Code No.:	Unknown
Size:	2 ¾", 7.0 cm
Backstamp:	K-1
Introduced:	1992-1992
Location:	Oakhanger, Hampshire
Series:	Anniversary Editions
Can.	$300.00
U.S.	$225.00
U.K.	£145.00

Note: Produced to commemorate the 10th anniversary of Lilliput Lane.

HONEYSUCKLE COTTAGE

Style Three

Code No.:	Unknown
Size:	1 ½", 3.9 cm
Backstamp:	None
Introduced:	1996-1996
Location:	Oakhanger, Hampshire
Series:	Dream Cottage Miniatures
Can.	$35.00
U.S.	$25.00
U.K.	£15.00

Note: Free with purchase of £29.95.

HONEYSUCKLE COTTAGE III

Style Four, First Version
(Without wall)

Code No.:	L2096A
Size:	2 ½", 6.4 cm
Backstamp:	P-1
Introduced:	1997-1997
Location:	Oakhanger, Hampshire
Series:	Visitor Centre Exclusive
Can.	$1,100.00
U.S.	$ 750.00
U.K.	£ 475.00

Note: Approx. 60-70 models exist.

Photograph not available at press time.

See previous image for shape outline.

HONEYSUCKLE COTTAGE III

Style Four, Second Version
(One row of brick around base)

Code No.:	L2096B
Size:	2 ½", 6.4 cm
Backstamp:	P-1
Introduced:	1997-1997
Location:	Oakhanger, Hampshire
Series:	Visitor Centre Exclusive
Can.	$575.00
U.S.	$400.00
U.K.	£250.00

Photograph not available at press time.

See previous image for shape outline

HONEYSUCKLE COTTAGE III

Style Four, Third Version
(Two rows of brick around base)

Code No.:	L2096C
Size:	2 ½", 6.4 cm
Backstamp:	P-1
Introduced:	1997 to the present
Location:	Oakhanger, Hampshire
Series:	Visitor Centre Exclusive
Can.	N/A
U.S.	N/A
U.K.	£24.95

HONEYSUCKLE TRINKET BOX

Code No.:	L2062
Size:	3 ½", 8.9 cm
Backstamp:	V
Introduced:	1997-1999
Location:	Oakhanger, Hampshire
Series:	Visitor Centre Special
Can.	$85.00
U.S.	$60.00
U.K.	£40.00

HOOK, LINE AND SINKER™

Code No.:	892
Size:	3 ½" , 8.9 cm
Backstamp:	N-2
Introduced:	1995-1999
Series:	Coca-Cola™ Country
Can.	$125.00
U.S.	$ 80.00
U.K.	£ 50.00

HOPCROFT COTTAGE

Code No.:	610
Size:	4", 10.1 cm
Backstamp:	J
Introduced:	1991-1995
Location:	Old Warden, Bedfordshire
Series:	English: South-East
Can.	$140.00
U.S.	$100.00
U.K.	£ 65.00

HOROLOGIST

Code No.:	L2050
Size:	5" , 12.7 cm
Backstamp:	P-1
Introduced:	1997-1999
Series:	Victorian Shops
Can.	$100.00
U.S.	$ 75.00
U.K.	£ 45.00

THE HOUSE OF THE TAILOR OF GLOUCESTER™

Code No.:	L2269
Size:	3 ½", 8.9 cm
Backstamp:	R
Introduced:	1999 to the present
Series:	Beatrix Potter™
Can.	N/A
U.S.	$65.00
U.K.	£28.50

HUBBLE-BUBBLE

Code No.:	L2132
Size:	2 ¾", 7.0 cm
Backstamp:	P-1
Introduced:	1998 to the present
Location:	Pendleton, Lancashire
Series:	English
Can.	$65.00
U.S.	$35.00
U.K.	£17.50

I PLEDGE ALLEGIANCE

Code No.:	L2075
Size:	3 ½", 8.9 cm
Backstamp:	O-2
Introduced:	1997-1999
Location:	Indiana
Series:	Allegiance
Can.	$95.00
U.S.	$70.00
U.K.	£45.00

I'LL BE HOME FOR CHRISTMAS

Code No.:	L2165
Size:	3 ½", 8.9 cm
Backstamp:	Unknown
Introduced:	1998 to the present
Location:	Topeka, Kansas
Series:	Allegiance
Can.	N/A
U.S.	$75.00
U.K.	£39.95

I.N. MONGERS & SONS

Code No.:	L2334
Size:	3 ½", 8.9 cm
Backstamp:	R
Introduced:	2000 to the present
Series:	English
Can.	$160.00
U.S.	$ 90.00
U.K.	£ 35.95

IN REMEMBRANCE

Code No.:	L2077
Size:	2 ¾", 7.0 cm
Backstamp:	O-2
Introduced:	1997-1999
Location:	Missouri
Series:	Allegiance
Can.	$95.00
U.S.	$65.00
U.K.	£40.00

INGLEWOOD

First Version (2 rear windows)

Code No.:	Unknown
Size:	2", 5.0 cm
Backstamp:	F
Introduced:	1987-1994
Location:	Near York
Series:	English: Northern
Can.	$90.00
U.S.	$65.00
U.K.	£40.00

INGLEWOOD

Second Version (1 rear window)

Code No.:	Unknown
Size:	2", 5.0 cm
Backstamp:	F
Introduced:	1989-1994
Location:	Near York
Series:	English: Northern
Can.	$60.00
U.S.	$40.00
U.K.	£25.00

Note: Slightly larger, with more pronounced windows and finer details.

INVERLOCHIE HAME

Code No.:	044
Size:	2 ½", 6.4 cm
Backstamp:	H-1
Introduced:	1989-1999
Location:	Scottish Highlands
Series:	Scottish
Can.	$65.00
U.S.	$50.00
U.K.	£30.00

IT'S A SMALL WORLD™

Code No.:	L2382
Size:	6" x 6" x 4½", 15.0 x 15.0 x 11.9 cm
Backstamp:	R
Introduced:	2000
Series:	Disneyana™
Can.	N/A
U.S.	$325.00
U.K.	N/A

IVY HOUSE

Code No.:	Unknown
Size:	3", 7.6 cm
Backstamp:	M
Introduced:	1994-1994
Series:	Christmas Annual Ornament
Can.	$45.00
U.S.	$30.00
U.K.	£20.00

IZAAK WALTON'S COTTAGE

Code No.:	Unknown
Size:	3 ½", 8.9 cm
Backstamp:	F
Introduced:	1987-1989
Series:	English: Midlands
Can.	$175.00
U.S.	$135.00
U.K.	£ 85.00

JAGDHÜTTE

Code No.:	252
Size:	4 ½", 11.9 cm
Backstamp:	F
Introduced:	1987-1998
Series:	German
Can.	$100.00
U.S.	$ 75.00
U.K.	£ 45.00

JASMINE COTTAGE

Style One - 5"

Code No.:	355A
Size:	5", 12.7 cm
Backstamp:	J
Introduced:	1991-1996
Location:	Bristol
Series:	1. Blaise Hamlet 2. English: South-West
Can.	$140.00
U.S.	$100.00
U.K.	£ 65.00

JASMINE COTTAGE
Style Two - 2 ¾"

Code No.:	355B
Size:	2 ¾", 7.0 cm
Backstamp:	L
Introduced:	1993-1995
Location:	Bristol
Series:	Classics
Can.	$100.00
U.S.	$ 75.00
U.K.	£ 45.00

Note: Early designs refer to this model as the "Dutch Cottage."

JEWELLER
First Version ("H. Samuel," No dog at foot of stairs)

Code No.:	L2107
Size:	4 ¾", 12.1 cm
Backstamp:	P-1
Introduced:	1997-1999
Location:	Knightsbridge, London
Series:	Victorian Shops
Can.	$65.00
U.S.	$50.00
U.K.	£30.00

JEWELLER
Second Version ("Jeweller," Dog at foot of stairs)

Code No.:	L2108
Size:	4 ¾", 12.1 cm
Backstamp:	P-1
Introduced:	1997-1999
Location:	Knightsbridge, London
Series:	Victorian Shops
Can.	$65.00
U.S.	$50.00
U.K.	£30.00

JINGLE BELLS

Code No.:	L2238
Size:	2 ¾", 7.0 cm
Backstamp:	R
Introduced:	1999-1999
Series:	Christmas Annual Ornament
Can.	$45.00
U.S.	$32.00
U.K.	£20.00

JOHN BARLEYCORN COTTAGE

Code No.:	606
Size:	4 ¼", 10.8 cm
Backstamp:	J
Introduced:	1991-1995
Location:	Old Warden, Bedfordshire
Series:	English: South-East
Can.	$150.00
U.S.	$110.00
U.K.	£ 70.00

JOHN KNOX HOUSE

Code No.:	Unknown
Size:	5 ¾", 14.6 cm
Backstamp:	H-1
Introduced:	19891-1992
Location:	Edinburgh
Series:	Scottish
Can.	$130.00
U.S.	$ 90.00
U.K.	£ 60.00

JONES THE BUTCHER

Code No.: 649
Size: 3 ¾", 9.5 cm
Backstamp: L
Introduced: 1993-1998
Location: Cotswolds
Series: Village Shops

Can. $100.00
U.S. $ 70.00
U.K. £ 45.00

JUNK AND DISORDERLY

Code No.: 152
Size: 4", 10.1 cm
Backstamp: L
Introduced: 1993-1998
Location: Pembridge, Herefordshire
Series: English: Midlands

Can. $140.00
U.S. $100.00
U.K. £ 65.00

KEEPER'S LODGE

Code No.: Unknown
Size: 3 ½", 8.9 cm
Backstamp: F
Introduced: 1987-1988
Series: English: Northern

Can. $140.00
U.S. $100.00
U.K. £ 65.00

KENDAL TEA HOUSE

Code No.: 71999/799
Size: 3 ¾", 9.5 cm
Backstamp: N-1
Introduced: 1995 to the present
Location: Sticklandgate, Kendal
Series: English Tea Rooms

Can. $140.00
U.S. $ 85.00
U.K. £ 39.95

KENMORE COTTAGE

Code No.: 487
Size: 3 ½", 8.9 cm
Backstamp: H-1
Introduced: 1989-1993
Location: Kenmore, Scotland
Series: Scottish

Can. $140.00
U.S. $100.00
U.K. £ 65.00

KENNEDY HOMESTEAD

Code No.: 468
Size: 2 ¼", 5.7 cm
Backstamp: H-1
Introduced: 1989-1996
Location: Dunganstown, County Wexford
Series: Irish

Can. $60.00
U.S. $40.00
U.K. £25.00

KENTISH BREW

Code No.: L2228
Size: 3 ½", 8.9 cm
Backstamp: R
Introduced: 1999 to the present
Series: English

Can. $60.00
U.S. $35.00
U.K. £17.50

KENTISH COTTAGE

Code No.: 760
Size: 2 ½", 6.4 cm
Backstamp: N-1
Introduced: 1995-1998
Series: Paint Your Own

Can. $45.00
U.S. $30.00
U.K. £20.00

Note: Prices refer to unpainted models, which are more valuable.

KENTISH OAST HOUSE

First Version (Plastic vanes)

Code No.: Unknown
Size: 3 ¾", 9.5 cm
Backstamp: D
Introduced: 1985-1990
Location: Tunbridge Wells, Kent
Series: English: South-East

Can. $700.00
U.S. $500.00
U.K. £325.00

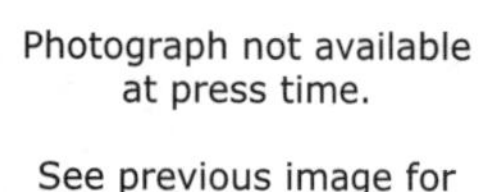

KENTISH OAST HOUSE

Second Version (Metal vanes)

Code No.: Unknown
Size: 3 ¾", 9.5 cm
Backstamp: D
Introduced: 1986-1990
Location: Tunbridge Wells, Kent
Series: English: South-East

Can. $140.00
U.S. $100.00
U.K. £ 65.00

KERRY LODGE

Code No.: 769
Size: 4", 10.1 cm
Backstamp: N-1
Introduced: 1995-1995
Location: Killarney, Ireland
Series: Christmas Lodge

Can. $140.00
U.S. $100.00
U.K. £ 65.00

KILMORE QUAY

Code No.: Unknown
Size: 2 ¾", 7.0 cm
Backstamp: H-1
Introduced: 1989-1992
Location: County Wexford
Series: Irish

Can. $130.00
U.S. $ 90.00
U.K. £ 60.00

KILN COTTAGE

Code No.:	L2124
Size:	2 ¾", 7.0 cm
Backstamp:	Q-2
Introduced:	1998-1999
Location:	Devon
Series:	Collectors Club
Can.	$50.00
U.S.	$35.00
U.K.	£20.00

Note: This model is a companion piece to The Pottery.

THE KING'S ARMS

Code No.:	419
Size:	5 ½", 14.0 cm
Backstamp:	I-1
Introduced:	1990-1995
Series:	English: South-East
Can.	$600.00
U.S.	$425.00
U.K.	£275.00

KINLOCHNESS

Code No.:	Unknown
Size:	4", 10.1 cm
Backstamp:	H-1
Introduced:	1990-1993
Series:	Scottish
Can.	$125.00
U.S.	$ 85.00
U.K.	£ 55.00

KIRKBRAE COTTAGE

Code No.:	495
Size:	2 ½", 6.4 cm
Backstamp:	H-1
Introduced:	1990-1993
Location:	Banffshire, Scotland
Series:	Scottish
Can.	$100.00
U.S.	$ 70.00
U.K.	£ 45.00

DIE KLEINE BÄCKEREI

Code No.:	Unknown
Size:	3 ½", 8.9 cm
Backstamp:	G
Introduced:	1988-1994
Series:	German
Can.	$100.00
U.S.	$ 70.00
U.K.	£ 45.00

LABOUR OF LOVE

Code No.:	L2235
Size:	3", 7.6 cm
Backstamp:	R
Introduced:	1999 to the present
Series:	Welsh
Can.	$100.00
U.S.	$ 55.00
U.K.	£ 25.95

LACE HOUSE

Code No.:	L2145
Size:	3 ¾", 9.5 cm
Backstamp:	P-1
Introduced:	1997-2000
Location:	Black Hawk, Colorado
Series:	An American Journey
Can.	N/A
U.S.	$85.00
U.K.	£55.95

LACE LANE

Code No.:	605
Size:	4", 10.1 cm
Backstamp:	J
Introduced:	1991-1997
Location:	Nottingham
Series:	English: Midlands
Can.	$100.00
U.S.	$ 75.00
U.K.	£ 50.00

LADY JANE'S COTTAGE

Code No.:	L2161
Size:	2 ¼", 5.7 cm
Backstamp:	Q-2
Introduced:	1998-2000
Location:	Irvine, Scotland
Series:	Scottish
Can.	$65.00
U.S.	$35.00
U.K.	£18.50

LADYBANK LODGE

Code No.:	695
Size:	3 ½", 8.9 cm
Backstamp:	M
Introduced:	1994-1998
Location:	Ladybank, Fife
Series:	Scottish
Can.	$70.00
U.S.	$50.00
U.K.	£30.00

LADYBIRD COTTAGE

Code No.:	791
Size:	2 ½", 6.4 cm
Backstamp:	N-1
Introduced:	1995-1998
Location:	Warkton, Northamptonshire
Series:	English: Midlands
Can.	$45.00
U.S.	$30.00
U.K.	£20.00

LAKESIDE HOUSE

First Version (27 windows, 10 roof tiles)

Code No.:	Unknown
Size:	4", 10.1 cm
Backstamp:	A-1, None
Introduced:	1982-1982
Location:	Lake District
Series:	English: Northern
Can.	$2,200.00
U.S.	$1,500.00
U.K.	£ 900.00

COLLECTORS CLUB

Cider Apple Cottage: Based on a cottage found close to the Somerset village of Selworthy, this model was the "Much Valued Customer" prize.

Fresh Today: This little farm shop is modelled from Wiltshire, and was the Club Symbol of Membership 1999/2000.

Hampton Manor: Marketed with *Hampton Moat*, *Hampton Manor* completes the set of two pieces. Both models are based in Lower Brockhampton, Herefordshire.

Hampton Moat: Available from March 1997 to February 1998, this model was based on a timber gatehouse that leads to the main building, *Hampton Manor*.

COLLECTORS CLUB

The Kiln Cottage: This potter's cottage is based on a property in Devon, and was the 1998-1999 Symbol of Membership.

Meadowsweet Cottage: Built in the 17th century at Elmley Castle in the Vale of Evesham, this model was available March 1996 through special order.

Porlock Down: Located in Selworthy, Somerset, *Porlock Down* was part of the Holnicote Estate built by Sir Thomas Dyke Aceland in the 19th century.

The Winnows: Constructed in the 16th century in Castle Combe, Wiltshire, this model was given to collectors who enrolled another member in the Collectors Club.

SPECIAL EDITIONS

Ashberry Cottage: Modelled after a Minchin cottage this model was produced for collectors who attended Lane Dinner at the 1992 South Bend Show.

Butterfly Cottage: The 1999/2000 Sales Promotion Special Edition, *Butterfly Cottage* illustrates the the Lilliput vernacular traditions of Buntingford.

Candy Cottage: This model, based on a cottage from Shanklin, was the 2000 Sales Promotion Special Edition.

Dormouse Cottage: Located in Inberrow, Worcestershire, this cottage was available at Special Events during 1997.

SPECIAL EDITIONS

Honeysuckle Cottage III: Based on the Visitors Centre, this model is available only to personal callers. Three versions of this cottage are known to exist.

Leagrave Cottage: This cottage was launched at the 1994 Lilliput Lane Annuel Fair and was available only in the year that followed.

Rainbow's End: Located in Alswear, Devon, this country cottage was the 1999 Sales Promotion Special Edition.

Rose Cottage, Skirsgill: This model is available only to personal callers at the Visitor Centre, Skirsgill, near Penrith.

NEW 2000 EDITIONS

Balmoral: This Scottish retreat is a favourite of Britain's Royal Family.

Beekeeper's Cottage: Located at Bridgewater Bay, this model was the 2000-2001 Club Special Edition.

Bill & Ben's: This cottage was inspired by a 17th century building from Alfriston.

Birthday Cottage: Rebuilt after a fire in the 1900s, this cottage was constructed in the 1890s for the keeper of an ornamental park in Lowestoft.

NEW 2000 EDITIONS

Burley Street Garage: This 17th century cottage allowed early motorists to stop off for petrol while out for a drive.

Chatterbox Corner: Romantic architectural features dominate this 18th century estate cottage, which belongs to the *English Collection.*

A Drop of the Irish: Part of the *Irish Collection,* this cottage is modelled after a ramshackle 15th century croft.

Home is Where the Heart Is: Exhibiting East Anglian vernacular style, this piece was modelled from a 16th century timber-framed cottage from Hadstock.

NEW 2000 EDITIONS

I.N. Mongers & Sons: Part of the *English Collection,* this cottage was inspired from a 17th century building in Stamford.

Little Bee: The 2000/2001 Club Symbol of Membership, *Little Bee* is a companion piece to the *Beekeeper's Cottage*.

Mother's Garden: This timber-framed house was inspired by an 18th century cottage from Houghton.

Nelson's Column: *Nelson's Column* is a monument that celebrates one of Britain's greatest navel heroes.

NEW 2000 EDITIONS

Pepper Mill Cottage: The mock-Tudor cottages of the Somerleyton estate formed the basis for this model, which is part of the *English Collection.*

The Royal Albert Hall: Belonging to the *Britain's Heritage* series, this model replicates one of the most prestigious concert halls in the United Kingdom.

The Royal Pavilion, Brighton: A remarkable piece of architecture, this model pays homage to John Nash's stunning design.

LAKESIDE HOUSE
Second Version (17 windows, 10 roof tiles)

Code No.:	Unknown
Size:	4", 10.1 cm
Backstamp:	A-1
Introduced:	1982-1983
Location:	Lake District
Series:	English: Northern
Can.	$900.00
U.S.	$600.00
U.K.	£375.00

Photograph not available at press time.

See previous page for shape outline.

LAKESIDE HOUSE
Third Version (17 windows, 6 roof tiles)

Code No.:	Unknown
Size:	3 ½", 8.9 cm
Backstamp:	A-2
Introduced:	1983-1986
Location:	Lake District
Series:	English: Northern
Can.	$700.00
U.S.	$500.00
U.K.	£300.00

Photograph not available at press time.

See previous page for shape outline.

LANGDALE COTTAGE

Code No.:	772
Size:	2 ½", 6.4 cm
Backstamp:	N-1
Introduced:	1995-1998
Location:	Lake District
Series:	Lakeland Christmas
Can.	$45.00
U.S.	$30.00
U.K.	£20.00

LAPWORTH LOCK

Code No.:	437
Size:	2 ¾", 7.0 cm
Backstamp:	J
Introduced:	1991-1993
Location:	Stratford-upon-Avon
Series:	English: Midlands
Can.	$125.00
U.S.	$ 80.00
U.K.	£ 50.00

LARKRISE

Code No.:	793
Size:	2 ¾", 7.0 cm
Backstamp:	N-1
Introduced:	1995-1998
Location:	Weekley, Northamptonshire
Series:	English: Midlands
Can.	$60.00
U.S.	$40.00
U.K.	£25.00

LAVENDER COTTAGE

Code No.:	Unknown
Size:	2 ¾", 7.0 cm
Backstamp:	H-1
Introduced:	1989-1991
Location:	Bishops Cannings, Wiltshire
Series:	Collectors Club
Can.	$140.00
U.S.	$100.00
U.K.	£ 65.00

LAVENDER LANE

Code No.: L2243
Size: 3 ½", 8.9 cm
Backstamp: R
Introduced: 1999 to the present
Series: English

Can. $120.00
U.S. $ 75.00
U.K. £ 29.95

LAZY DAYS

Code No.: 797
Size: 3", 7.6 cm
Backstamp: N-1
Introduced: 1995-1998
Location: Letcombe Regis, Oxfordshire
Series: English: South-West

Can. $75.00
U.S. $50.00
U.K. £30.00

LEAGRAVE COTTAGE

Code No.: 729
Size: 3 ½", 8.9 cm
Backstamp: M
Introduced: 1994-1995
Location: Buckinghamshire
Series: Special Editions

Can. $175.00
U.S. $125.00
U.K. £ 80.00

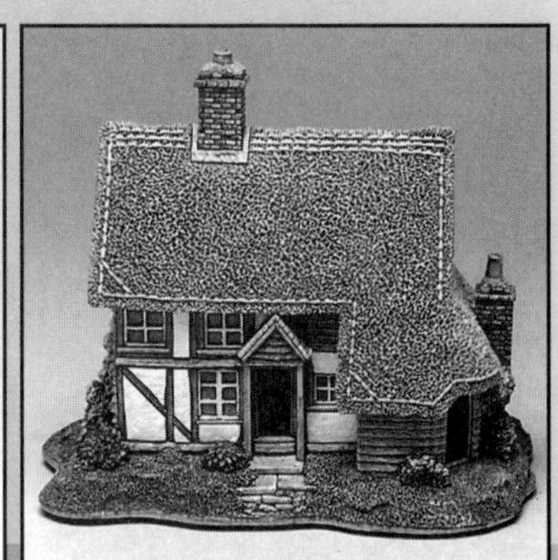

LEONORA'S SECRET

Code No.: 727
Size: 4 ½", 11.9 cm
Backstamp: Limited Edition
Introduced: 1994 in a limited edition of 2,500
Series: Garden

Can. $700.00
U.S. $500.00
U.K. £325.00

LET HEAVEN AND NATURE SING

Code No.: 2065
Size: 5", 12.7 cm
Backstamp: P-1
Introduced: 1997-1997
Location: Port Gamble, Washington
Series: Christmas in America

Can. $175.00
U.S. $125.00
U.K. £ 80.00

"LIBERTY ENLIGHTENING THE WORLD"

Code No.: 723185
Size: 5" x 5" x 8 ¾", 12.7 x 12.7 x 22.2 cm
Backstamp: R
Introduced: 2000 to the present
Location: New York City
Series: American Treasures

Can. N/A
U.S. $55.00
U.K. N/A

LIGHTHOUSE

Code No.:	Unknown
Size:	4", 10.1 cm
Backstamp:	C
Introduced:	1984-1985
Location:	New England
Series:	American (1st)
Can.	$1,300.00
U.S.	$ 875.00
U.K.	£ 600.00

Note: Approximately 200 models were produced.

LILAC LODGE

Code No.:	L2090
Size:	3", 7.6 cm
Backstamp:	P-1
Introduced:	1997 to the present
Location:	Lyme Regis, Dorset
Series:	English
Can.	$100.00
U.S.	$ 60.00
U.K.	£ 28.50

LIMERICK HOUSE

Code No.:	Unknown
Size:	3 ¾", 9.5 cm
Backstamp:	H-1
Introduced:	1989-1992
Location:	Adare, County Limerick
Series:	Irish
Can.	$140.00
U.S.	$100.00
U.K.	£ 65.00

THE LION HOUSE

Code No.:	L2187
Size:	4 ¼", 10.8 cm
Backstamp:	Q-2
Introduced:	1998 to the present
Series:	English
Can.	$100.00
U.S.	$ 70.00
U.K.	£ 25.95

LITTLE BEE

Code No.:	L2317
Size:	3 ¼", 8.3 cm
Backstamp:	R
Introduced:	2000-2001
Series:	Collectors Club
Can.	N/A
U.S.	N/A
U.K.	N/A

Note: Free with Collectors Club Membership.

LITTLE BIRCH

Code No.:	L2104
Size:	3 ½", 8.9 cm
Backstamp:	Unknown
Introduced:	1997 to the present
Series:	Paint Your Own
Can.	N/A
U.S.	$25.00
U.K.	£20.00

Note: Prices refer to unpainted models, which are more valuable.

LITTLE HAY

Code No.:	795
Size:	2 ½", 6.4 cm
Backstamp:	N-1
Introduced:	1995-1998
Location:	Newnham, Northhamptonshire
Series:	English: Midlands
Can.	$60.00
U.S.	$40.00
U.K.	£25.00

LITTLE LUPINS

Code No.:	003
Size:	2 ¾", 7.0 cm
Backstamp:	O-1
Introduced:	1996-1999
Location:	Suffolk
Series:	English: South-East
Can.	$50.00
U.S.	$35.00
U.K.	£20.00

LITTLE SMITHY

Code No.:	796
Size:	2 ½", 6.4 cm
Backstamp:	N-1
Introduced:	1995-1999
Location:	Claverdon
Series:	English: Midlands
Can.	$80.00
U.S.	$55.00
U.K.	£35.00

LITTLE WATER MILL

Code No.:	L2227
Size:	3", 7.6 cm
Backstamp:	R
Introduced:	1999 to the present
Series:	English
Can.	$100.00
U.S.	$ 55.00
U.K.	£ 25.95

LOBSTER AT THE PIER

Code No.:	L2120
Size:	4 ¼", 10.8 cm
Backstamp:	P-1
Introduced:	1997-2000
Location:	New England
Series:	American Landmarks
Can.	N/A
U.S.	$90.00
U.K.	£45.95

LOCH NESS LODGE

Code No.:	L2175
Size:	3 ¾", 9.5 cm
Backstamp:	Q-2
Introduced:	1998 to the present
Series:	Scottish
Can.	$250.00
U.S.	$170.00
U.K.	£ 59.95

LOCMARIA

Code No.: 423
Size: 4″, 10.1 cm
Backstamp: I-2
Introduced: 1990-1997
Location: Brittany, France
Series: French

Can. $70.00
U.S. $50.00
U.K. £30.00

LOG CABIN

First Version (With snow)

Code No.: Unknown
Size: 1 ¾″, 4.4 cm
Backstamp: C
Introduced: 1984-1985
Series: American (1st)

Can. $1,000.00
U.S. $ 750.00
U.K. £ 475.00

Note: Only 150 models (First and Second Versions) were produced.

LOG CABIN

Second Version (Without snow)

Code No.: Unknown
Size: 1 ¾″, 4.4 cm
Backstamp: C
Introduced: 1985-1985
Series: American (1st)

Can. $850.00
U.S. $600.00
U.K. £375.00

Note: Only 150 models (First and Second Versions) were produced.

LOXDALE COTTAGE

Code No.: 002
Size: 3 ¾″, 9.5 cm
Backstamp: O-1
Introduced: 1996-1999
Location: Thornton-le-Dale, North Yorkshire
Series: English: Northern

Can. $45.00
U.S. $30.00
U.K. £20.00

LUCKY CHARMS

Code No.: L2222
Size: 2 ½″, 6.4 cm
Backstamp: R
Introduced: 1999 to the present
Series: English

Can. $55.00
U.S. $35.00
U.K. £15.50

"THE LUNCH LINE"™

Code No.: L2069
Size: 2 ½″, 6.4 cm
Backstamp: O-2
Introduced: 1997-2000
Series: Coca-Cola™ Country

Can. $60.00
U.S. $40.00
U.K. £35.00

MAGIC KINGDOM® TRAIN STATION /MAGIC KINGDOM MEMORIES™

Code No.:	Unknown
Size:	Unknown
Backstamp:	Unknown
Introduced:	1998-1998
Series:	Disneyana™
Can.	N/A
U.S.	$750.00
U.K.	N/A

MAGILLIGAN'S

Code No.:	471
Size:	2", 5.0 cm
Backstamp:	H-1
Introduced:	1989-1996
Location:	County Derry, Ireland
Series:	Irish
Can.	$45.00
U.S.	$30.00
U.K.	£20.00

MAGPIE COTTAGE
First Variation (Cream shed)

Code No.:	Unknown
Size:	3 ¼", 8.3 cm
Backstamp:	F
Introduced:	1987-1989
Location:	Herefordshire
Series:	English: Midlands
Can.	$100.00
U.S.	$ 75.00
U.K.	£ 50.00

MAGPIE COTTAGE
Second Variation (Pink shed)

Code No.:	Unknown
Size:	3 ¼", 8.3 cm
Backstamp:	F
Introduced:	1989-1990
Location:	Herefordshire
Series:	English: Midlands
Can.	$100.00
U.S.	$ 75.00
U.K.	£ 50.00

MAIL POUCH BARN

Code No.:	523
Size:	3 ¼", 8.3 cm
Backstamp:	H-1
Introduced:	1989-1993
Location:	Hendricks County, Indiana
Series:	American Landmarks
Can.	$140.00
U.S.	$100.00
U.K.	£ 65.00

MAIN STREET CINEMA™

Code No.:	L2303
Size:	4", 10.1 cm; 5 ¼", 13.3 cm (with flag)
Backstamp:	Unknown
Introduced:	1999-1999
Series:	Disneyana™
Can.	N/A
U.S.	$275.00
U.K.	N/A

MAIR HAVEN

Code No.:	490
Size:	2 ½″, 6.4 cm
Backstamp:	K-1
Introduced:	1992-1999
Series:	Scottish
Can.	$50.00
U.S.	$35.00
U.K.	£25.00

MAKE A WISH

Code No.:	L2342
Size:	2 ¼″, 5.7 cm
Backstamp:	R
Introduced:	1999 to the present
Series:	English
Can.	N/A
U.S.	N/A
U.K.	N/A

Note: Complimentary gift with purchase of Lilliput Lane products.

MANGERT

Code No.:	
Size:	
Backstamp:	U
Introduced:	19
Location:	Brid
Series:	Englis
Can.	$225.0
U.S.	$165.00
U.K.	£100.00

LE MANOIR DE CHAMPFLEURI

Code No.:	425
Size:	6 ¾″, 17.2 cm
Backstamp:	I-2
Introduced:	1990-1997
Location:	Loire Valley, France
Series:	French
Can.	$300.00
U.S.	$200.00
U.K.	£125.00

MARBLE ARCH

Code No.:	L2289
Size:	3 ½″, 8.9 cm
Backstamp:	R
Introduced:	1999 to the present
Location:	London
Series:	Britain's Heritage™
Can.	N/A
U.S.	$60.00
U.K.	£25.95

MARCHE HOUSE

Code No.:	L2083
Size:	2 ¾″, 7.0 cm
Backstamp:	Unknown
Introduced:	1997 to the present
Series:	Paint Your Own
Can.	N/A
U.S.	N/A
U.K.	£15.00

Note: Prices refer to unpainted models, which are more valuable.

LE MAS DU VIGNERON

ode No.: 430
ze: 3 ½", 8.9 cm
kstamp: I-2
duced: 1990-1997
on: Provence, France
French

$135.00
$ 95.00
£ 60.00

LA MASELLE DE NADAILLAC

Code No.: 426
Size: 4", 10.1 cm
Backstamp: I-2
Introduced: 1990-1997
Location: Dordogne, France
Series: French

Can. $135.00
U.S. $ 95.00
U.K. £ 60.00

MAYFLOWER HOUSE

First Variation (Grey windows)

Code No.: Unknown
Size: 4 ½", 11.9 cm
Backstamp: H-1
Introduced: 1989-1990
Location: Lavenham, Suffolk
Series: Special Editions

Can. $475.00
U.S. $325.00
U.K. £200.00

MAYFLOWER HOUSE

Second Variation (Blue windows)

Code No.: Unknown
Size: 4 ½", 11.9 cm
Backstamp: H-1
Introduced: 1989-1990
Location: Lavenham, Suffolk
Series: Special Editions

Can. $450.00
U.S. $300.00
U.K. £185.00

MEADOWSWEET COTTAGE

Code No.: 861
Size: 3 ¾", 9.5 cm
Backstamp: O-2
Introduced: 1996-1997
Location: Vale of Evesham
Series: Collectors Club

Can. $140.00
U.S. $100.00
U.K. £ 65.00

MEDWAY MANOR

Code No.:	L2082
Size:	4 ¼", 10.8 cm
Backstamp:	P-1
Introduced:	1998-1999
Location:	Smarden, Kent
Series:	English
Can.	$140.00
U.S.	$100.00
U.K.	£ 60.00

MEERSBURGER WEINSTUBE

Code No.:	251
Size:	4 ¾", 12.1 cm
Backstamp:	F
Introduced:	1987-1998
Series:	German
Can.	$90.00
U.S.	$65.00
U.K.	£40.00

MICKLEGATE ANTIQUES

Code No.:	566
Size:	4 ¼", 10.8 cm
Backstamp:	J
Introduced:	1991-1997
Location:	York
Series:	English: Northern
Can.	$100.00
U.S.	$ 75.00
U.K.	£ 50.00

MICKLEGATE BAR, YORK

Code No.:	L2209
Size:	4", 10.1 cm
Backstamp:	Q-2
Introduced:	1998 to the present
Location:	York
Series:	Britain's Heritage™
Can.	$65.00
U.S.	$37.00
U.K.	£16.50

MIDHURST

Code No.:	L2205
Size:	4", 10.1 cm
Backstamp:	R
Introduced:	1999-1999
Series:	Helen Allingham
Can.	$100.00
U.S.	$100.00
U.K.	£ 45.00

MIDWEST BARN

Code No.:	Unknown
Size:	2 ½", 6.4 cm
Backstamp:	C
Introduced:	1984-1985
Series:	American (1st)
Can.	$450.00
U.S.	$300.00
U.K.	£200.00

Note: 400 models were produced.

MILESTONE COTTAGE

Code No.:	792
Size:	2 ½", 6.4 cm
Backstamp:	N-1
Introduced:	1995-1999
Location:	Harlestone, Northamptonshire
Series:	English: Midlands
Can.	$45.00
U.S.	$30.00
U.K.	£20.00

"MILK FOR MOM AND A COKE FOR ME™"

Code No.:	L2166
Size:	3 ½", 8.9 cm
Backstamp:	Unknown
Introduced:	1998-2000
Location:	New Albany, Indiana
Series:	Coca-Cola™ Country
Can.	N/A
U.S.	$95.00
U.K.	£60.00

MILLBECK

Code No.:	844
Size:	2 ¾", 7.0 cm
Backstamp:	O-1
Introduced:	1996-1999
Location:	Millbeck, Cumbria
Series:	Lakeland Christmas
Can.	$45.00
U.S.	$30.00
U.K.	£20.00

Photograph not available at press time.

See next page for shape outline.

Photograph not available at press time.

See next page for shape outline.

THE MILLENNIUM GATE

Code No.:	L2170
Size:	5 ½", 14.0 cm
Backstamp:	R
Introduced:	1999 in a limited edition of 2,000
Series:	Millennium
Can.	N/A
U.S.	$500.00
U.K.	£195.00

MILLERS

First Version, First Variation (8 panes)

Code No.:	Unknown
Size:	2 ½", 6.4 cm
Backstamp:	A-1
Introduced:	1983-1983
Location:	Kent
Series:	English: South-East
Can.	$450.00
U.S.	$300.00
U.K.	£200.00

MILLERS

First Version, Second Variation (8 panes, smaller)

Code No.:	Unknown
Size:	2 ½", 6.4 cm
Backstamp:	C
Introduced:	1983-1984
Location:	Kent
Series:	English: South-East
Can.	$450.00
U.S.	$300.00
U.K.	£200.00

MILLERS
Second Version (6 Panes)

Code No.:	Unknown
Size:	2 ½", 6.4 cm
Backstamp:	B
Introduced:	1984-1986
Location:	Kent
Series:	English: South-East
Can.	$200.00
U.S.	$135.00
U.K.	£ 85.00

MINERS COTTAGE / MINERS
First Version, First Variation (Grey)

Code No.:	Unknown
Size:	2 ¾", 7.0 cm
Backstamp:	A-1
Introduced:	1983-1983
Location:	Kent
Series:	English: Northern
Can.	$950.00
U.S.	$675.00
U.K.	£425.00

Note: Originally named Miners Cottage.

MINERS COTTAGE / MINERS
First Version, Second Variation (Sandy roof)

Code No.:	Unknown
Size:	2 ¾", 7.0 cm
Backstamp:	A-1
Introduced:	1983-1983
Location:	Kent
Series:	English: Northern
Can.	$950.00
U.S.	$675.00
U.K.	£425.00

Note: Originally named Miners Cottage.

MINERS COTTAGE / MINERS
First Version, Third Variation (Black roof)

Code No.:	Unknown
Size:	2 ¾", 7.0 cm
Backstamp:	A-1
Introduced:	1983-1983
Location:	Kent
Series:	English: Northern
Can.	$950.00
U.S.	$675.00
U.K.	£425.00

Note: Originally named Miners Cottage.

MINERS COTTAGE / MINERS
Second Version, First Variation (Sandy roof)

Code No.:	Unknown
Size:	2 ½", 6.4 cm
Backstamp:	B
Introduced:	1983-1984
Location:	Kent
Series:	English: Northern
Can.	$575.00
U.S.	$400.00
U.K.	£200.00

Note: Renamed Miners.

MINERS COTTAGE / MINERS
Second Version, Second Variation (Black roof)

Code No.:	Unknown
Size:	2 ½", 6.4 cm
Backstamp:	B
Introduced:	1983-1985
Location:	Kent
Series:	English: Northern
Can.	$575.00
U.S.	$400.00
U.K.	£200.00

Note: Renamed Miners.

MINERS COTTAGE / MINERS

Second Version, Third Variation
(Olive roof)

Code No.:	Unknown
Size:	2 ½", 6.4 cm
Backstamp:	B
Introduced:	1983-1985
Location:	Kent
Series:	English: Northern
Can.	$575.00
U.S.	$400.00
U.K.	£200.00

Note: Renamed Miners.

MISTLETOE COTTAGE

Code No.:	Unknown
Size:	2 ½", 6.4 cm
Backstamp:	K-1
Introduced:	1992-1992
Location:	Kent
Series:	Christmas Annual Ornament
Can.	$50.00
U.S.	$35.00
U.K.	£20.00

"MMM . . . JUST LIKE HOME"™

Code No.:	L2073
Size:	3 ½", 8.9 cm
Backstamp:	O-2
Introduced:	1997-1999
Series:	Coca-Cola™ Country
Can.	$140.00
U.S.	$ 95.00
U.K.	£ 60.00

Note: Exclusive to North America, this model is cast in resin and is hand-numbered.

MOONLIGHT COVE

Code No.:	438
Size:	3 ¾", 9.5 cm
Backstamp:	J
Introduced:	1991-1996
Location:	Cornwall
Series:	English: South-West
Can.	$80.00
U.S.	$55.00
U.K.	£35.00

MORETON MANOR

Code No.:	Unknown
Size:	3 ½", 8.9 cm
Backstamp:	D
Introduced:	1985-1989
Location:	Moreton-in-the-Marsh
Series:	English: Midlands
Can.	$200.00
U.S.	$135.00
U.K.	£ 85.00

MORNING HAS BROKEN

Code No.:	L2150
Size:	3 ¾", 8.3 cm
Backstamp:	P-1
Introduced:	1997 to the present
Location:	Babcock State Park, West Virginia
Series:	An American Journey
Can.	N/A
U.S.	$85.00
U.K.	£45.95

MOSELHAUS

Code No.:	256
Size:	5 ½", 14.0 cm
Backstamp:	F
Introduced:	1987-1998
Series:	German
Can.	$175.00
U.S.	$125.00
U.K.	£ 80.00

MOSSWOOD

Code No.:	L2179
Size:	2 ½ ", 6.4 cm
Backstamp:	Q-2
Introduced:	1998 to the present
Series:	English
Can.	$120.00
U.S.	$ 85.00
U.K.	£ 29.95

MOTHER'S GARDEN

Code No.:	L2323
Size:	2 ½", 6.4 cm
Backstamp:	R
Introduced:	2000 to the present
Series:	English
Can.	$50.00
U.S.	$30.00
U.K.	£13.50

MRS. PINKERTON'S POST OFFICE

Code No.:	504
Size:	3 ¼", 9.5 cm
Backstamp:	H-1
Introduced:	1989-1997
Series:	English: South-East
Can.	$90.00
U.S.	$60.00
U.K.	£40.00

NATURE'S BOUNTY

Code No.:	L2263
Size:	4 ½", 11.9 cm
Backstamp:	R
Introduced:	1999 to the present
Series:	American Landmarks
Can.	N/A
U.S.	$140.00
U.K.	£ 55.95

NATURE'S DOORWAY

Code No.:	L2251
Size:	5", 12.7 cm
Backstamp:	R
Introduced:	1999 to the present
Series:	Secret Gardens™
Can.	$160.00
U.S.	$ 90.00
U.K.	£ 39.95

NELSON'S COLUMN

Code No.:	L2253
Size:	7 ¾", 19.7 cm
Backstamp:	R
Introduced:	2000 to the present
Location:	London
Series:	Britain's Heritage™
Can.	$70.00
U.S.	$55.00
U.K.	£19.95

NELSON'S COLUMN IN WINTER

Code No.:	L2301
Size:	7 ½", 19.1 cm
Backstamp:	R
Introduced:	1999-2000
Location:	London
Series:	Millennium
Can.	N/A
U.S.	$60.00
U.K.	£25.95

NEST EGG

Code No.:	L2255
Size:	2 ¼", 5.7 cm
Backstamp:	Q-2
Introduced:	1998-1998
Series:	Special Edition
Can.	$45.00
U.S.	$30.00
U.K.	£20.00

NEW FOREST TEAS

Code No.:	798
Size:	3 ¾", 9.5 cm
Backstamp:	N-1
Introduced:	1995-1999
Location:	Brockenhurst, Hampshire
Series:	English Tea Rooms
Can.	$165.00
U.S.	$120.00
U.K.	£ 75.00

NEW NEIGHBOURS

Code No.:	L2229
Size:	3 ½", 8.9 cm
Backstamp:	R
Introduced:	1999 to the present
Series:	English
Can.	$140.00
U.S.	$ 85.00
U.K.	£ 35.95

NIGHTINGALE

Code No.:	L2130
Size:	2 ¼", 5.7 cm
Backstamp:	Q-1
Introduced:	1998-2000
Location:	Duddington, Northamptonshire
Series:	English
Can.	$40.00
U.S.	$25.00
U.K.	£ 9.95

LA NORMANDIE

Code No.:	Unknown
Size:	Unknown
Backstamp:	Q-2
Introduced:	1998-1998
Series:	Special Edition
Can.	$150.00
U.S.	$110.00
U.K.	£ 70.00

Photograph not available at press time

"NOTHING RUNS LIKE A DEERE"™

Code No.:	L2216
Size:	3 ½", 8.9 cm
Backstamp:	Q-2
Introduced:	1998 to the present
Series:	America's Favourites
Can.	N/A
U.S.	$37.50
U.K.	N/A

NÜRNBERGER BÜRGERHAUS

Code No.:	254
Size:	5", 12.7 cm
Backstamp:	B
Introduced:	1987-1998
Series:	German
Can.	$175.00
U.S.	$125.00
U.K.	£ 80.00

NURSERY COTTAGE

First Variation (Without EEGG)

Code No.:	Unknown
Size:	4", 10.1 cm
Backstamp:	O-1
Introduced:	1996-1996
Location:	Lamarsh, Suffolk
Series:	Collectors Club
Can.	$90.00
U.S.	$60.00
U.K.	£40.00

NURSERY COTTAGE

Second Variation (With EEGG)

Code No.:	Unknown
Size:	4", 10.1 cm
Backstamp:	O-2
Introduced:	1996-1997
Location:	Lamarsh, Suffolk
Series:	Collectors Club
Can.	$140.00
U.S.	$100.00
U.K.	£ 60.00

THE NUTSHELL

Code No.:	634
Size:	2 ¾", 7.0 cm
Backstamp:	K-1
Introduced:	1992-1995
Location:	Mersea Island, Essex
Series:	English: South-East
Can.	$90.00
U.S.	$60.00
U.K.	£40.00

OAK COTTAGE
First Version - 4 ½″

Code No.:	118
Size:	4 ½″, 11.9 cm
Backstamp:	H-1
Introduced:	1989-1993
Location:	Bristol
Series:	Blaise Hamlet
Can.	$175.00
U.S.	$125.00
U.K.	£ 80.00

OAK COTTAGE
Second Version - 2 ½″

Code No.:	Unknown
Size:	2 ½″, 6.4 cm
Backstamp:	L
Introduced:	1993-1995
Location:	Bristol
Series:	Classics
Can.	$100.00
U.S.	$ 75.00
U.K.	£ 45.00

OAK LODGE
Style One, First Version
(7 rows of roof tiles, less foliage)

Code No.:	Unknown
Size:	3″, 7.6 cm
Backstamp:	None, A-1, A-2
Introduced:	1982-1983
Series:	English: South-East
Can.	$700.00
U.S.	$500.00
U.K.	£300.00

Photograph not available at press time.

See next image for shape outline.

OAK LODGE
Style One, Second Version
(5 rows of roof tiles, more foliage)

Code No.:	Unknown
Size:	3″, 7.6 cm
Backstamp:	C
Introduced:	1983-1987
Series:	English: South-East
Can.	$125.00
U.S.	$ 90.00
U.K.	£ 55.00

Note: The roof overhang on the left-hand side was also reduced.

OAK LODGE
Style Two

Code No.:	Unknown
Size:	4 ½″, 11.9 cm
Backstamp:	L
Introduced:	1993
Location:	Wrecclesham
Series:	Special Editions
Can.	$2,250.00
U.S.	$1,600.00
U.K.	£1,000.00

Note: The Oak Lodge award was given to employees with 10 years of service.

OAKWOOD SMITHY

Code No.:	616
Size:	4 ¾″, 12.1 cm
Backstamp:	K-1
Introduced:	1992-1999
Series:	English: South-East
Can.	$375.00
U.S.	$275.00
U.K.	£175.00

OCTAGON TOWER

Code No.:	Unknown
Size:	4 ¼″, 10.8 cm
Backstamp:	M
Introduced:	1994 in a limited edition of 5,000
Series:	Studley Royal
Can.	$100.00
U.S.	$ 75.00
U.K.	£ 45.00

OH BY GOSH, BY GOLLY™

Code No.:	L2085
Size:	Unknown
Backstamp:	Unknown
Introduced:	1997-1997
Series:	Coca-Cola™ Country
Can.	$95.00
U.S.	$70.00
U.K.	£45.00

O'LACEY'S STORE

Code No.:	466
Size:	3″, 7.6 cm
Backstamp:	H-1
Introduced:	1989-1996
Location:	County Mayo
Series:	Irish
Can.	$75.00
U.S.	$50.00
U.K.	£30.00

OLD CROFTY

Code No.:	L2231
Size:	4″, 10.1 cm
Backstamp:	R
Introduced:	1999 to the present
Series:	English
Can.	$140.00
U.S.	$ 85.00
U.K.	£ 35.95

THE OLD CURIOSITY SHOP

First Variation (Green windows)

Code No.:	055A
Size:	3 ½″, 8.9 cm
Backstamp:	D
Introduced:	1985-1989
Location:	London
Series:	English: South-East
Can.	$125.00
U.S.	$ 85.00
U.K.	£ 55.00

THE OLD CURIOSITY SHOP

Second Variation (Tan windows)

Code No.:	055B
Size:	3 ½″, 8.9 cm
Backstamp:	D
Introduced:	1985-1989
Location:	London
Series:	English: South-East
Can.	$125.00
U.S.	$ 85.00
U.K.	£ 55.00

THE OLD FORGE

Code No.:	L2133
Size:	2 ¾", 7.0 cm
Backstamp:	P-1
Introduced:	1998 to the present
Location:	Queniborough, Leicestershire
Series:	English
Can.	$100.00
U.S.	$ 55.00
U.K.	£ 25.95

OLD MILL

Code No.:	Unknown
Size:	3 ½", 8.9 cm
Backstamp:	A-1
Introduced:	1982-1982
Series:	English: South-West
Can.	$4,000.00
U.S.	$3,000.00
U.K.	£1,750.00

Note: It was soon realized that the model was a mine and not a mill, and was quickly renamed Old Mine. Approximately 10 pieces were produced.

OLD MINE

Code No.:	Unknown
Size:	3 ½", 8.9 cm
Backstamp:	A-1
Introduced:	1982-1983
Series:	English: South-West
Can.	$4,000.00
U.S.	$3,000.00
U.K.	£1,500.00

Note: Only 200 models were produced.

Photograph not available at press time.

See next page for shape outline.

OLD MOTHER HUBBARD'S

First Version - 3 ½"

Code No.:	660A
Size:	3 ½", 8.9 cm
Backstamp:	L
Introduced:	1993-1999
Location:	Yealmpton, Devon
Series:	English: South-West
Can.	$140.00
U.S.	$100.00
U.K.	£ 65.00

OLD MOTHER HUBBARD'S

Second Version - 1½"

Code No.:	Unknown
Size:	1 ½", 3.5 cm
Backstamp:	None
Introduced:	1997-1999
Location:	Yealmpton, Devon
Series:	Dream Cottage Miniatures
Can.	$45.00
U.S.	$30.00
U.K.	£20.00

THE OLD POST OFFICE

First Version (Less foliage, backstamp A-1)

Code No.:	Unknown
Size:	2 ¾", 7.0 cm
Backstamp:	A-1
Introduced:	1982-1982
Series:	English: South-West
Can.	$1,000.00
U.S.	$ 750.00
U.K.	£ 475.00

THE OLD POST OFFICE
Second Version (Less foliage, backstamp A-2)

Code No.:	Unknown
Size:	2 ¾″, 7.0 cm
Backstamp:	A-2
Introduced:	1982-1983
Series:	English: South-West
Can.	$750.00
U.S.	$525.00
U.K.	£350.00

THE OLD POST OFFICE
Third Version (More foliage, backstamps B and C)

Code No.:	Unknown
Size:	2 ¾″, 7.0 cm
Backstamp:	B, C
Introduced:	1983-1986
Varieties:	Tintagel
Series:	English: South-West
Can.	$675.00
U.S.	$475.00
U.K.	£300.00

THE OLD ROYAL OBSERVATORY

Code No.:	L2245
Size:	5 ½″, 14.0 cm
Backstamp:	R
Introduced:	1999 in a limited edition of 2,000
Series:	Millennium
Can.	N/A
U.S.	N/A
U.K.	£150.00

Photograph not available at press time.

See next image for shape outline.

Photograph not available at press time.

See next image for shape outline.

OLD SCHOOL HOUSE
First Version (Smaller tower)

Code No.:	Unknown
Size:	2 ½″, 6.4 cm
Backstamp:	A-1
Introduced:	1984-1985
Varieties:	Cliburn School
Series:	English: Northern
Can.	$1,600.00
U.S.	$1,100.00
U.K.	£ 700.00

OLD SCHOOL HOUSE
Second Version (Larger tower)

Code No.:	Unknown
Size:	2 ½″, 6.4 cm
Backstamp:	D
Introduced:	1984-1985
Varieties:	Cliburn School
Series:	English: Northern
Can.	$1,100.00
U.S.	$ 800.00
U.K.	£ 500.00

OLD SHOP AT BIGNOR

Code No.:	611
Size:	4 ½″, 11.9 cm
Backstamp:	J
Introduced:	1991-1995
Location:	Bignor
Series:	English: South-East
Can.	$250.00
U.S.	$175.00
U.K.	£110.00

OLD STATE HOUSE, 1776

Code No.: 723150
Size: 4 ¼" x 3 ¾" x 4 ¾", 10.8 x 9.5 x 12.1 cm
Backstamp: R
Introduced: 2000 to the present
Series: America's National Treasures

Can. N/A
U.S. $50.00
U.K. N/A

THE OLD VICARAGE AT CHRISTMAS

Code No.: 620
Size: 4 ½", 11.9 cm
Backstamp: J
Introduced: 1991-1991
Series: Christmas Specials

Can. $200.00
U.S. $150.00
U.K. £ 95.00

OLDE YORK TOLL

Code No.: Unknown
Size: 4 ½", 11.9 cm
Backstamp: I-1
Introduced: 1989-1991
Location: York
Series: Special Editions

Can. $175.00
U.S. $125.00
U.K. £ 80.00

ONE NATION UNDER GOD

Code No.: L2078
Size: 4", 10.1 cm
Backstamp: P-1
Introduced: 1997-1999
Varieties: Country Church, Style Two
Location: Thomaston, Maine
Series: Allegiance

Can. $100.00
U.S. $ 75.00
U.K. £ 45.00

ORCHARD FARM COTTAGE

Code No.: 670
Size: 3 ¼", 9.5 cm
Backstamp: M
Introduced: 1994-1998
Location: Hever, Kent
Series: English: South-East

Can. $140.00
U.S. $100.00
U.K. £ 65.00

OSTLERS KEEP

Code No.: 065
Size: 2 ¾", 7.0 cm
Backstamp: D
Introduced: 1985-1991
Location: Devon
Series: English: South-West

Can. $100.00
U.S. $ 75.00
U.K. £ 45.00

OTTER REACH

Code No.:	412
Size:	2 ½", 6.4 cm
Backstamp:	I-2
Introduced:	1990-1996
Location:	Devon
Series:	English: South-West
Can.	$45.00
U.S.	$30.00
U.K.	£20.00

"OUR FIRST TELLY"

Code No.:	L2201
Size:	5 ¼", 13.3 cm
Backstamp:	Q-2
Introduced:	1998-1999
Series:	Moments in Time
Can.	$170.00
U.S.	$100.00
U.K.	£ 50.00

OUT FOR A DUCK

Code No.:	L2274
Size:	3 ¼", 9.5 cm
Backstamp:	R
Introduced:	1999 to the present
Series:	English
Can.	N/A
U.S.	$75.00
U.K.	£29.95

OUT OF THE STORM

Code No.:	L2064
Size:	9 ¼", 23.5 cm
Backstamp:	P-1
Introduced:	1997 in a limited edition of 3,000
Location:	Clovelly, North Devon
Series:	English: South-West
Can.	$1,750.00
U.S.	$1,250.00
U.K.	£ 800.00

PAINSWICK POST OFFICE

Code No.:	L2039
Size:	3 ¾", 9.5 cm
Backstamp:	O-2
Introduced:	1996-1998
Series:	Paint Your Own
Can.	$45.00
U.S.	$30.00
U.K.	£20.00

Note: Prices refer to unpainted models, which are more valuable.

PARADISE LODGE

First Version - 4 ½"

Code No.:	608A
Size:	4 ½", 11.9 cm
Backstamp:	J
Introduced:	1991-1996
Location:	Shropshire
Series:	English: Midlands
Can.	$130.00
U.S.	$ 90.00
U.K.	£ 55.00

PARADISE LODGE
Second Version - 1 ½″

Code No.: Unknown
Size: 1 ½″, 3.9 cm
Backstamp: None
Introduced: 1997-1999
Location: Shropshire
Series: Dream Cottage Miniatures

Can. $45.00
U.S. $30.00
U.K. £20.00

PARGETTER'S RETREAT

Code No.: Unknown
Size: 4 ½″, 11.9 cm
Backstamp: G
Introduced: 1988-1990
Location: East Anglia
Series: English: South-East

Can. $130.00
U.S. $ 90.00
U.K. £ 55.00

PARSON'S RETREAT

Code No.: L2138
Size: 4 ¼″, 10.8 cm
Backstamp: P-2
Introduced: 1998-2000
Location: Clare, Suffolk
Series: English

Can. $160.00
U.S. $ 90.00
U.K. £ 45.95

PARTRIDGE COTTAGE

Code No.: 643
Size: 2 ½″, 6.4 cm
Backstamp: L
Introduced: 1993-1997
Location: Cotswolds
Series: Christmas

Can. $50.00
U.S. $35.00
U.K. £25.00

PASTURES NEW

Code No.: L2142
Size: 5 ¼″, 13.3 cm
Backstamp: P-2
Introduced: 1998 to the present
Location: Duddington, Northamptonshire
Series: English

Can. $500.00
U.S. $350.00
U.K. £135.00

PAT COHAN'S BAR

Code No.: 464
Size: 3 ½″, 8.9 cm
Backstamp: H-1
Introduced: 1989-1996
Location: County Mayo, Ireland
Series: Irish

Can. $110.00
U.S. $ 80.00
U.K. £ 50.00

PATTERDALE COTTAGE

Code No.: 771
Size: 2 ¾″, 7.0 cm
Backstamp: N-1
Introduced: 1995-1998
Location: Lake District
Series: Lakeland Christmas

Can. $45.00
U.S. $30.00
U.K. £20.00

PAWNBROKER

Code No.: L2052
Size: 5 ¼″, 13.3 cm
Backstamp: P-1
Introduced: 1997-1999
Location: Buxton, Derbyshire
Series: Victorian Shops

Can. $90.00
U.S. $65.00
U.K. £40.00

PEACEFUL PASTIMES

Code No.: L2194
Size: 3 ½″, 8.9 cm
Backstamp: Q-2
Introduced: 1998 to the present
Series: Secret Gardens™

Can. $150.00
U.S. $ 90.00
U.K. £ 39.95

PEAR TREE HOUSE

Code No.: 435
Size: 3 ¼″, 8.3 cm
Backstamp: J
Introduced: 1991-1995
Location: Mansellacey, Herefordshire
Series: English: Midlands

Can. $100.00
U.S. $ 70.00
U.K. £ 45.00

PEN PALS

Code No.: L2241
Size: 4 ¼″, 10.8 cm
Backstamp: R
Introduced: 1999-1999
Series: Anniversary

Can. $250.00
U.S. $170.00
U.K. £ 65.00

PENKILL CASTLE

Code No.: 820
Size: 3 ¾″, 9.5 cm
Backstamp: N-2
Introduced: 1995-1998
Series: Historic Castles of Britain

Can. $140.00
U.S. $100.00
U.K. £ 65.00

PENNY'S POST

Code No.: 794
Size: 2 ½", 6.4 cm
Backstamp: N-1
Introduced: 1995 to the present
Location: Adlesetrop, Gloucestershire
Series: English: Midlands

Can. $70.00
U.S. $55.00
U.K. £19.95

PENNY SWEETS

Code No.: 593
Size: 3 ½", 8.9 cm
Backstamp: K-1
Introduced: 1992-1998
Location: Gloucestershire
Series: Village Shops

Can. $100.00
U.S. $ 70.00
U.K. £ 45.00

DE PEPERMOLEN

Code No.: 122
Size: 4 ¾", 12.1 cm
Backstamp: J
Introduced: 1991-1998
Variation: Begijnhof
Series: Netherlands

Can. $50.00
U.S. $35.00
U.K. £25.00

Note: De Pepermolen's roof is grey and white, while Begijnhof's is brown.

PEPPER MILL COTTAGE

Code No.: L2330
Size: 3 ¼", 8.3 cm
Backstamp: R
Introduced: 2000 to the present
Series: English

Can. $80.00
U.S. $50.00
U.K. £19.95

PEPSI COLA™ BARN

Code No.: 528
Size: 3", 7.6 cm
Backstamp: I-2
Introduced: 1990-1991
Location: Madison, Indiana
Series: American Landmarks

Can. $225.00
U.S. $165.00
U.K. £100.00

PERIWINKLE COTTAGE

Code No.: 508
Size: 4 ½", 11.9 cm
Backstamp: I-2
Introduced: 1990-1996
Location: Selworthy
Series: English: South-West

Can. $225.00
U.S. $160.00
U.K. £ 95.00

LE PETIT MONTMARTRE

Code No.:	428
Size:	5″, 12.7 cm
Backstamp:	I-2
Introduced:	1990-1997
Location:	Paris
Series:	French
Can.	$140.00
U.S.	$100.00
U.K.	£ 65.00

PETTICOAT COTTAGE

Code No.:	Unknown
Size:	2 ½″, 6.4 cm
Backstamp:	M
Introduced:	1994-1995
Location:	Hampshire
Series:	Collectors Club
Can.	$50.00
U.S.	$35.00
U.K.	£25.00

PICNIC PARADISE

Code No.:	L2195
Size:	4 ¼″, 10.8 cm
Backstamp:	Q-2
Introduced:	1998 to the present
Series:	Secret Gardens™
Can.	$130.00
U.S.	$ 80.00
U.K.	£ 35.95

THE PINEAPPLE HOUSE

Code No.:	L2118
Size:	3 ¾″, 9.5 cm
Backstamp:	Q-1
Introduced:	1998 to the present
Series:	Scottish
Can.	$75.00
U.S.	$60.00
U.K.	£19.95

PIONEER BARN

Code No.:	527
Size:	1 ¾″, 4.4 cm
Backstamp:	I-1
Introduced:	1990-1991
Location:	Indiana
Series:	American Landmarks
Can.	$90.00
U.S.	$65.00
U.K.	£40.00

PIPIT TOLL

Code No.:	778
Size:	3″, 7.65 cm
Backstamp:	N-1
Introduced:	1995-1998
Location:	Codford, Wiltshire
Series:	English: South-West
Can.	$55.00
U.S.	$40.00
U.K.	£25.00

PIXIE HOUSE

Code No.:	612
Size:	2 ¼", 5.7 cm
Backstamp:	K-1
Introduced:	1992-1995
Location:	Cornwall
Series:	English: South-West
Can.	$60.00
U.S.	$45.00
U.K.	£25.00

THE PLANETARIUM

Code No.:	L2246
Size:	4 ¾", 12.1 cm
Backstamp:	R
Introduced:	1999-2000
Series:	Millennium
Can.	$360.00
U.S.	$210.00
U.K.	£ 89.95

PLAYTIME

Code No.:	L2277
Size:	3 ¼", 8.3 cm
Backstamp:	R
Introduced:	1999 to the present
Series:	English
Can.	N/A
U.S.	$75.00
U.K.	£29.95

PLOUGHMAN'S COTTAGE

Code No.:	Unknown
Size:	3", 7.6 cm
Backstamp:	K-1
Introduced:	1992-1993
Location:	Nobottle, Northamptonshire
Series:	Special Events
Can.	$110.00
U.S.	$ 80.00
U.K.	£ 50.00

PLUM COTTAGE

Code No.:	768
Size:	2", 5.0 cm
Backstamp:	N-2
Introduced:	1995-1995
Series:	Christmas Annual Ornament
Can.	$45.00
U.S.	$30.00
U.K.	£20.00

THE POPPIES

Code No.:	L2058
Size:	3", 7.6 cm
Backstamp:	P-1
Introduced:	1997 to the present
Location:	Pebworth, Worcestershire
Series:	English
Can.	$75.00
U.S.	$50.00
U.K.	£19.95

PORLOCK DOWN

Code No.:	766
Size:	4", 10.1 cm
Backstamp:	N-1
Introduced:	1995-1996
Location:	Selworthy, Somerset
Series:	Collectors Club
Can.	$175.00
U.S.	$125.00
U.K.	£ 80.00

LA PORTE SCHOENENBERG

Code No.:	421
Size:	4", 10.1 cm
Backstamp:	I-2
Introduced:	1990-1997
Series:	French
Can.	$90.00
U.S.	$65.00
U.K.	£40.00

POTTERS BECK

Code No.:	L2003
Size:	2 ½", 6.4 cm
Backstamp:	O-2
Introduced:	1996-1998
Location:	North Yorkshire
Series:	English: Northern
Can.	$45.00
U.S.	$30.00
U.K.	£20.00

THE POTTERY

Code No.:	L2123
Size:	4", 10.1 cm
Backstamp:	R
Introduced:	1998-1999
Location:	Devon
Series:	Collectors Club
Can.	$175.00
U.S.	$135.00
U.K.	£ 85.00

Note: This model is a companion piece to the Kiln Cottage.

THE PRESIDENT'S HOUSE/ WHITE HOUSE

Code No.:	723169
Size:	4 ¾" x 4 ¾" x 2 ¾", 12.1 x 12.1 x 7.0 cm
Backstamp:	R
Introduced:	2000 to the present
Location:	Washington, D.C.
Series:	America's National Treasures
Can.	N/A
U.S.	$45.00
U.K.	N/A

PRESTON MILL

First Version (Short Roof)

Code No.:	Unknown
Size:	3 ½", 8.9 cm
Backstamp:	D
Introduced:	1985-1986
Location:	East Linton, Scotland
Series:	Scottish
Can.	$225.00
U.S.	$175.00
U.K.	£125.00

Note: This version had rear stairs, a side barn door and a short pantiled roof.

PRESTON MILL
Second Version (Tall Roof)

Code No.: Unknown
Size: 3 ½", 8.9 cm
Backstamp: F
Introduced: 1986-1992
Series: Scottish

Can. $140.00
U.S. $100.00
U.K. £ 65.00

Note: This version has a water mill, foliage at the rear, and a tall, sectioned pantiled roof.

THE PRIEST'S HOUSE

Code No.: 601
Size: 5", 12.7 cm
Backstamp: J
Introduced: 1991-1995
Location: Prestbury, Cheshire
Series: English: Northern

Can. $225.00
U.S. $165.00
U.K. £100.00

PRIMROSE HILL

Code No.: 433
Size: 3", 7.6 cm
Backstamp: L
Introduced: 1991-996
Location: Chiddingstone, Kent
Series: English: South-East

Can. $50.00
U.S. $35.00
U.K. £25.00

LA PROVENCE

Code No.: Unknown
Size: 2 ¾", 7.0 cm
Backstamp: Q-2
Introduced: 1998-1998
Series: Special Edition

Can. $150.00
U.S. $110.00
U.K. £ 70.00

PUDDLEBROOK

Code No.: Unknown
Size: 2 ½", 6.4 cm
Backstamp: J
Introduced: 1991-1992
Series: Collectors Club

Can. $60.00
U.S. $40.00
U.K. £25.00

PUDDLE DUCK

Code No.: L2136
Size: 3 ¾", 9.5 cm
Backstamp: P-2
Introduced: 1998-2000
Location: Kersey, Suffolk
Series: English

Can. $130.00
U.S. $ 80.00
U.K. £ 35.95

PUFFIN ROW

Code No.:	615
Size:	3 ¼", 8.3 cm
Backstamp:	K-1
Introduced:	1992-1997
Location:	Boscastle, Cornwall
Series:	English: South-West
Can.	$125.00
U.S.	$ 85.00
U.K.	£ 55.00

PURBECK STORES

Code No.:	312
Size:	2 ½", 6.4 cm
Backstamp:	L
Introduced:	1993-1997
Location:	Dorset
Series:	English: South-West
Can.	$45.00
U.S.	$30.00
U.K.	£20.00

PUSSY WILLOW

Code No.:	Unknown
Size:	2 ½", 6.4 cm
Backstamp:	K-1
Introduced:	1992-1993
Location:	Flat Fenlands, Cambridgeshire
Series:	Collectors Club
Can.	$70.00
U.S.	$50.00
U.K.	£30.00

QUEEN ALEXANDRA'S NEST

Code No.:	Unknown
Size:	3 ½", 8.9 cm
Backstamp:	R
Introduced:	1999-1999
Series:	Special Edition
Can.	$165.00
U.S.	$115.00
U.K.	£ 70.00

QUIET COTTAGE

Code No.:	Unknown
Size:	2 ½", 6.4 cm
Backstamp:	H-1
Introduced:	1989-1992
Location:	County Galway
Series:	Irish
Can.	$110.00
U.S.	$ 80.00
U.K.	£ 50.00

RAILWAY COTTAGE

Code No.:	005
Size:	3 ½", 8.9 cm
Backstamp:	O-2
Introduced:	1996-1999
Location:	Edensor, Derbyshire
Series:	English: Midlands
Can.	$70.00
U.S.	$50.00
U.K.	£30.00

RAINBOW'S END

Code No.:	L2240
Size:	3", 7.6 cm
Backstamp:	R
Introduced:	1999-2000
Series:	Special Edition
Can.	N/A
U.S.	$55.00
U.K.	£24.95

RAMBLING ROSE

Code No.:	554
Size:	2 ½", 6.4 cm
Backstamp:	J
Introduced:	1991-1995
Location:	Nantucket Island, Massachusetts
Series:	American Landmarks
Can.	$90.00
U.S.	$65.00
U.K.	£40.00

DAS RATHAUS

Code No.:	258
Size:	5 ½", 14.0 cm
Backstamp:	G
Introduced:	1988-1998
Location:	Michelstadt, Germany
Series:	German
Can.	$175.00
U.S.	$135.00
U.K.	£ 85.00

READING COTTAGE

Code No.:	Unknown
Size:	3", 7.6 cm
Backstamp:	M
Introduced:	1994-1996
Series:	Paint Your Own
Can.	$45.00
U.S.	$30.00
U.K.	£20.00

RED LION INN

Code No.:	Unknown
Size:	5 ¼", 13.3 cm
Backstamp:	B
Introduced:	1983-1987
Location:	York
Series:	English: Northern
Can.	$525.00
U.S.	$375.00
U.K.	£250.00

REFLECTIONS OF JADE

Code No.:	012
Size:	4", 10.5 cm
Backstamp:	Special limited edition
Introduced:	1996 in a limited edition of 3,950
Series:	Garden
Can.	$475.00
U.S.	$325.00
U.K.	£200.00

Note: Prices refer to unpainted models, which are more valuable.

REMBRANDT VAN RIJN

Code No.: 125
Size: 6", 15.0 cm
Backstamp: J
Introduced: 1991-1998
Location: Breestraat, Holland
Series: Netherlands

Can. $100.00
U.S. $ 75.00
U.K. £ 45.00

REMEMBER THE ALAMO

Code No.: 723207
Size: 4 ½" x 4 ½" x 2 ½", 11.9 x 11.9 x 6.4 cm
Backstamp: R
Introduced: 2000 to the present
Series: America's National Treasures

Can. N/A
U.S. $45.00
U.K. N/A

THE RIGHT NOTE

Code No.: L2230
Size: 3 ½", 8.9 cm
Backstamp: R
Introduced: 1999 to the present
Series: English

Can. $140.00
U.S. $ 85.00
U.K. £ 35.95

RING O' BELLS

Code No.: 676
Size: 2 ¾", 7.0 cm
Backstamp: M
Introduced: 1994-1997
Series: Christmas

Can. $45.00
U.S. $30.00
U.K. £20.00

THE RISING SUN

Code No.: Unknown
Size: 2 ¼", 5.7 cm
Backstamp: G
Introduced: 1988-1992
Location: Ickford
Series: English: South-East

Can. $90.00
U.S. $65.00
U.K. £40.00

RIVERSIDE CHAPEL

Code No.: 530
Size: 3 ½", 8.9 cm
Backstamp: I-2
Introduced: 1990-1993
Location: Corydon, Indiana
Series: American Landmarks

Can. $175.00
U.S. $125.00
U.K. £ 80.00

RIVERVIEW

First Version (Plain roof, grey rocks)

Code No.:	300A
Size:	2″, 5.0 cm
Backstamp:	F
Introduced:	1987-1990
Location:	Welshpool
Series:	English: Midlands
Can.	$90.00
U.S.	$65.00
U.K.	£40.00

RIVERVIEW

Second Version (Finer roof, beige rocks)

Code No.:	300B
Size:	2″, 5.0 cm
Backstamp:	F
Introduced:	1990-1994
Location:	Welshpool
Series:	English: Midlands
Can.	$60.00
U.S.	$40.00
U.K.	£25.00

ROADSIDE COOLERS

Code No.:	Unknown
Size:	3″, 7.6 cm
Backstamp:	I-2
Introduced:	1990-1994
Location:	Huron, Indiana
Series:	American Landmarks
Can.	$135.00
U.S.	$ 95.00
U.K.	£ 60.00

Photograph not available at press time.

See previous image for shape outline.

ROBIN COTTAGE

Code No.:	644
Size:	2 ½″, 6.4 cm
Backstamp:	L
Introduced:	1993-1993
Series:	Christmas Annual Ornament
Can.	$50.00
U.S.	$35.00
U.K.	£25.00

ROBINS GATE

Code No.:	413
Size:	2 ½″, 6.4 cm
Backstamp:	I-2
Introduced:	1990-1996
Location:	Staffordshire
Series:	English: Midlands
Can.	$45.00
U.S.	$30.00
U.K.	£25.00

ROCK-A-BYE-BABY

Code No.:	L2223
Size:	2 ½″, 6.4 cm
Backstamp:	R
Introduced:	1999 to the present
Series:	English
Can.	$55.00
U.S.	$35.00
U.K.	£15.50

RODING HEATH / HIGH RODING

Code No.:	Unknown
Size:	3 ½", 8.9 cm
Backstamp:	M
Introduced:	1994-1996
Series:	Paint Your Own
Can.	$70.00
U.S.	$50.00
U.K.	£30.00

Note: Prices refer to unpainted models, which are more valuable.

ROSE BOUQUET

Code No.:	L2092
Size:	2", 5.0 cm
Backstamp:	P-1
Introduced:	1997 to the present
Location:	Wareham, Dorset
Series:	English
Can.	$40.00
U.S.	$25.00
U.K.	£ 9.95

ROSE COTTAGE
Style One - 4 ½"

Code No.:	353
Size:	4 ½", 11.9 cm
Backstamp:	J
Introduced:	1991-1997
Location:	Bristol
Series:	1. Blaise Hamlet 2. English: South-West
Can.	$140.00
U.S.	$100.00
U.K.	£ 65.00

ROSE COTTAGE
Style Two, First Version - 2 ½"

Code No.:	Unknown
Size:	2 ½", 6.4 cm
Backstamp:	L
Introduced:	1993-1995
Location:	Bristol
Series:	Classics
Can.	$100.00
U.S.	$ 75.00
U.K.	£ 45.00

ROSE COTTAGE
Style Two, Second Version - 1 ½"

Code No.:	Unknown
Size:	1 ½", 3.2 cm
Backstamp:	None
Introduced:	1997-1999
Location:	Bristol
Series:	Dream Cottage Miniatures
Can.	$45.00
U.S.	$30.00
U.K.	£20.00

ROSE COTTAGE, SKIRSGILL
Style One (Without dog)

Code No.:	623A
Size:	3", 7.6 cm
Backstamp:	J
Introduced:	1991-1991
Location:	Skirsgill
Series:	Special Editions
Can.	$675.00
U.S.	$475.00
U.K.	£300.00

ROSE COTTAGE, SKIRSGILL
Style Two (With dog)

Code No.:	623B
Size:	3", 7.6 cm
Backstamp:	J
Introduced:	1991-1994
Location:	Skirsgill
Series:	Special Editions
Can.	$325.00
U.S.	$225.00
U.K.	£150.00

ROSE COTTAGE, SKIRSGILL
Style Three (Added foliage)

Code No.:	623C
Size:	3", 7.6 cm
Backstamp:	M
Introduced:	1994 to the present
Location:	Skirsgill
Series:	Visitor Centre Exclusive
Can.	$175.00
U.S.	$125.00
U.K.	£ 80.00

ROSEMARY COTTAGE

Code No.:	007
Size:	3", 7.6 cm
Backstamp:	O-2
Introduced:	1996-1999
Location:	Northampton
Series:	English: Midlands
Can.	$85.00
U.S.	$60.00
U.K.	£35.00

ROSENGARTENHAUS

Code No.:	261
Size:	2 ¾", 7.0 cm
Backstamp:	K-1
Introduced:	1992-1998
Location:	Hamburg, Germany
Series:	German
Can.	$110.00
U.S.	$ 80.00
U.K.	£ 50.00

ROSY RAFTERS

Code No.:	L2019
Size:	3 ¾", 9.5 cm
Backstamp:	O-2
Introduced:	1996-1997
Series:	Paint Your Own
Can.	$45.00
U.S.	$30.00
U.K.	£25.00

Note: Prices refer to unpainted models, which are more valuable.

ROUND TOWER, WINDSOR CASTLE

Code No.:	L2212
Size:	3 ¾", 9.5 cm
Backstamp:	Q-2
Introduced:	1998 to the present
Location:	Windsor
Series:	Britain's Heritage™: Royal Residences
Can.	$80.00
U.S.	$50.00
U.K.	£19.95

ROWAN LODGE
First Variation (South Bend)

Code No.:	Unknown
Size:	3 ½", 8.9 cm
Backstamp:	I-2
Introduced:	1990-1990
Series:	Special Editions

Can.	$450.00
U.S.	$325.00
U.K.	£200.00

Note: Introduced at the South Bend Show U.S., 350 pieces were stamped "SOUTH BEND 90."

ROWAN LODGE
Second Variation (Collectors Club)

Code No.:	Unknown
Size:	3 ½", 8.9 cm
Backstamp:	I-2
Introduced:	1990-1991
Series:	Special Editions

Can.	$140.00
U.S.	$100.00
U.K.	£ 65.00

Note: Members could have the door painted in the colour of their choice.

THE ROYAL ALBERT HALL

Code No.:	L2311
Size:	2 ¾", 7.0 cm
Backstamp:	R
Introduced:	2000 to the present
Location:	London
Series:	Britain's Heritage™

Can.	$95.00
U.S.	$70.00
U.K.	£25.95

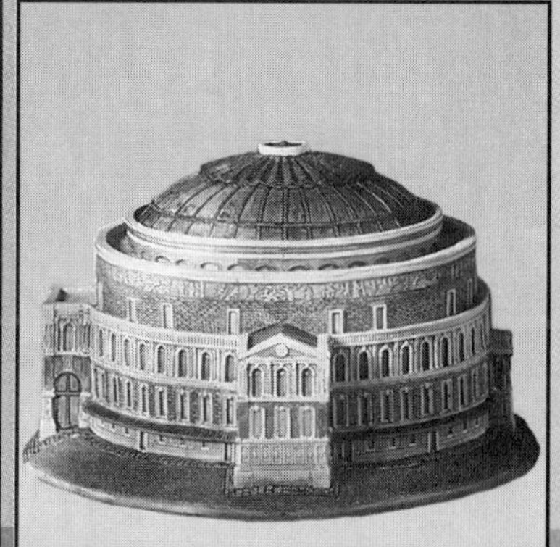

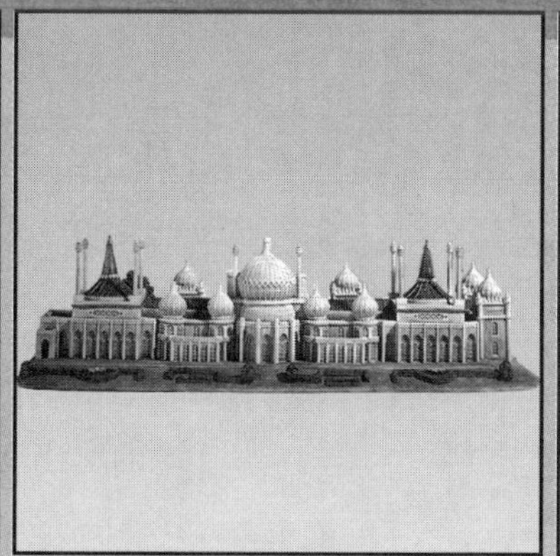

ROYAL OAK INN

Code No.:	Unknown
Size:	4 ¼", 10.1 cm
Backstamp:	G
Introduced:	1988-1991
Location:	Exmoor
Series:	English: South-West

Can.	$250.00
U.S.	$175.00
U.K.	£110.00

THE ROYAL PAVILION BRIGHTON

Code No.:	L2313
Size:	3", 7.6 cm
Backstamp:	R
Introduced:	2000 to the present
Location:	Brighton
Series:	Britain's Heritage™

Can.	$190.00
U.S.	$125.00
U.K.	£ 49.95

ROZENGRACHT

Code No.:	124
Size:	4 ¼", 10.8 cm
Backstamp:	J
Introduced:	1991-1998
Location:	Amsterdam, Holland
Series:	Netherlands

Can.	$60.00
U.S.	$45.00
U.K.	£30.00

RUBY COTTAGE

Code No.:	L2097
Size:	3 ¾", 9.5 cm
Backstamp:	Unknown
Introduced:	1998
Series:	Paint Your Own
Can.	$45.00
U.S.	$30.00
U.K.	£20.00

Note: Prices refer to unpainted models, which are more valuable.

RUNSWICK HOUSE

Code No.:	415
Size:	3 ¼", 8.3 cm
Backstamp:	I-2
Introduced:	1990-1998
Location:	East Yorkshire
Series:	English: Northern
Can.	$60.00
U.S.	$45.00
U.K.	£30.00

RUSTIC ROOT HOUSE

Code No.:	618
Size:	3 ¼", 8.3 cm
Backstamp:	K-1
Introduced:	1992-1997
Location:	Badminton
Series:	English: Midlands
Can.	$100.00
U.S.	$ 70.00
U.K.	£ 45.00

THE RUSTLINGS

Code No.:	776
Size:	3 ½", 8.9 cm
Backstamp:	N-1
Introduced:	1995-1998
Location:	Longstock, Hampshire
Series:	English: South-East
Can.	$100.00
U.S.	$ 70.00
U.K.	£ 45.00

RYDAL COTTAGE

Code No.:	770
Size:	2 ½", 6.4 cm
Backstamp:	N-1
Introduced:	1995-1998
Location:	Cumbria
Series:	Lakeland Christmas
Can.	$45.00
U.S.	$30.00
U.K.	£20.00

RYDAL VIEW

Code No.:	Unknown
Size:	5 ¼", 13.3 cm
Backstamp:	F
Introduced:	1987-1989
Location:	Lake District
Series:	English: Northern
Can.	$250.00
U.S.	$175.00
U.K.	£110.00

SADDLER'S INN

Code No.:	Unknown
Size:	3", 7.6 cm
Backstamp:	F
Introduced:	1987-1989
Location:	Staffordshire
Series:	English: Midlands
Can.	$90.00
U.S.	$65.00
U.K.	£40.00

SAFE HARBOR

Code No.:	L2154
Size:	4 ¼", 10.8 cm
Backstamp:	P-1
Introduced:	1997 in a limited edition of 1,783
Location:	Brewster Island, Massachusetts
Series:	An American Journey
Can.	N/A
U.S.	$75.00
U.K.	£29.95

SAFFRON HOUSE

Code No.:	666
Size:	4 ¼", 10.8 cm
Backstamp:	M
Introduced:	1994-1997
Location:	Saffron Walden, Essex
Series:	English: South-East
Can.	$225.00
U.S.	$165.00
U.K.	£100.00

SALMON'S LEAP

Code No.:	L2233
Size:	2 ¾", 7.0 cm
Backstamp:	R
Introduced:	1999 to the present
Series:	Scottish
Can.	$80.00
U.S.	$55.00
U.K.	£19.95

SAN FRANCISCO HOUSE

First Variation (Pink walls)

Code No.:	Unknown
Size:	4 ¼", 10.8 cm
Backstamp:	C
Introduced:	1984-1985
Series:	American (1st)
Can.	$1,100.00
U.S.	$ 800.00
U.K.	£ 500.00

Note: One blue model is known to exist.

SAN FRANCISCO HOUSE

Second Variation (Yellow walls)

Code No.:	Unknown
Size:	4 ¼", 10.8 cm
Backstamp:	C
Introduced:	1984-1985
Series:	American (1st)
Can.	$625.00
U.S.	$425.00
U.K.	£275.00

Note: A total of 400 pieces of this model were produced.The majority are the Second Variation.

THE SANDCASTLE

Code No.: L2324
Size: 3 ¼", 8.3 cm
Backstamp: R
Introduced: 2000 to the present
Series: English

Can. $50.00
U.S. $35.00
U.K. £13.50

SANTA'S CORNER™

Code No.: 518
Size: 3", 7.6 cm
Backstamp: O-2
Introduced: 1996 in a limited edition of 19,960
Series: 1. Coca Cola™ Country
2. Christmas Annual Ornament

Can. $50.00
U.S. $35.00
U.K. £25.00

SATURDAY NIGHT JIVE™

Code No.: L2074
Size: 3 ¾", 9.5 cm
Backstamp: O-2
Introduced: 1997-1999
Location: Silver Creek, Indiana
Series: Coca Cola™ Country

Can. $125.00
U.S. $ 85.00
U.K. £ 55.00

SAWREY GILL

Code No.: Unknown
Size: 2 ½", 6.4 cm
Backstamp: D
Introduced: 1985-1992
Series: English: Northern

Can. $130.00
U.S. $ 90.00
U.K. £ 60.00

SAXHAM ST. EDMUNDS

Code No.: Unknown
Size: 6", 15.0 cm
Backstamp: Ltd. Ed.
Introduced: 1991-1994
Series: English: South-East

Can. $1,650.00
U.S. $1,200.00
U.K. £ 750.00

Note: Only 1,828 models were produced.

SAXON COTTAGE

Code No.: Unknown
Size: 5 ½", 14.0 cm
Backstamp: G
Introduced: 1988-1989
Location: Steyning, East Sussex
Series: English: South-East

Can. $275.00
U.S. $200.00
U.K. £135.00

SAY IT WITH FLOWERS

Code No.: L2236
Size: 2 ¾″, 7.0 cm
Backstamp: R
Introduced: 1999 to the present
Series: English

Can. $65.00
U.S. $35.00
U.K. £17.50

SCHOOL DAYS

Code No.: 553
Size: 2 ¾″, 7.0 cm
Backstamp: J
Introduced: 1991-1997
Location: Hartser and Fairplay, Colorado
Series: American Landmarks

Can. $70.00
U.S. $50.00
U.K. £30.00

SCHWARZWALDHAUS

Code No.: 255
Size: 4 ¼″, 10.8 cm
Backstamp: F
Introduced: 1987-1998
Series: German

Can. $140.00
U.S. $100.00
U.K. £ 65.00

SCOTCH MIST

Code No.: L2159
Size: 2 ¾″, 7.0 cm
Backstamp: P-2
Introduced: 1998 to the present
Location: Oban, Scotland
Series: Scottish

Can. $120.00
U.S. $ 70.00
U.K. £ 29.95

SCOTNEY CASTLE GARDEN

Code No.: L2103
Size: 4″, 10.1 cm
Backstamp: P-2
Introduced: 1997 in a limited edition of 4,500
Series: English

Can. $350.00
U.S. $250.00
U.K. £165.00

SEAVIEW

Code No.: L2191
Size: 4 ¼″, 10.8 cm
Backstamp: Q-2
Introduced: 1998-2000
Series: Bed and Breakfast

Can. N/A
U.S. $80.00
U.K. £30.00

SECRET GARDEN

Code No.:	Unknown
Size:	5 ½", 14.0 cm
Backstamp:	F
Introduced:	1987-1994
Series:	English: Northern
Can.	$250.00
U.S.	$175.00
U.K.	£110.00

SEE ROCK CITY

Code No.:	656
Size:	2 ¾", 7.0 cm
Backstamp:	L
Introduced:	1993-1997
Series:	American Landmarks
Can.	$50.00
U.S.	$35.00
U.K.	£25.00

"SEE THE USA IN YOUR CHEVROLET"™

Code No.:	L2219
Size:	3", 7.6 cm
Backstamp:	Q-2
Introduced:	1998 to the present
Series:	America's Favourites
Can.	N/A
U.S.	$37.50
U.K.	N/A

SEEK AND FIND

Code No.:	L2121
Size:	4 ¼", 10.8 cm
Backstamp:	P-1
Introduced:	1997-2000
Location:	Welaka, Florida
Series:	American Landmarks
Can.	N/A
U.S.	$80.00
U.K.	£35.95

SETTLER'S SURPRISE

Code No.:	Unknown
Size:	2 ¼", 5.7 cm
Backstamp:	J
Introduced:	1991-1996
Location:	Auckland, New Zealand
Series:	Special Edition
Can.	$250.00
U.S.	$185.00
U.K.	£125.00

SEVEN DWARF'S COTTAGE™

Code No.:	Unknown
Size:	5 ¼", 13.3 cm
Backstamp:	None
Introduced:	1986 in a limited edition of 470
Series:	Disneyana™
Can.	$1,350.00
U.S.	$ 950.00
U.K.	£ 600.00

THE ALLEGIANCE COLLECTION by Ray Day

By Dawn's Early Light: Introduced in 1998, this model is based on the Mukilteo Lighthouse at Point Elliot in Puget Sound, Washington.

Fourth of July: This piece was inspired by Victorian bandstand celebrations in Bellville, Ohio.

I'll Be Home For Christmas: This model is set in a World War II-era train station in Ottawa Junction, southeast of Topeka, Kansas.

Stars and Stripes Forever: *Stars and Stripes Forever* is based on the home of Betsy Ross in Philadelphia, Pennsylvania.

AMERICA'S FAVOURITES by Ray Day

"Nothing Runs Like a Deere"™: Based on a barn from Indiana, this building also serves as an advertisement for John Deere tractors.

"See the USA in Your Chevrolet"™: Modelling a Chevrolet dealership, this piece was introduced in 1998.

"This Bud's For You"™: Typical of many businesses across America, this building was based on a tavern in New Albany, Indiana.

"Trust Your Car to the Star"™: Gas stations, like this one from Milltown, Indiana, replaced general stores across America.

AMERICAN COLLECTION

Country Church, First Variation

Country Church, Second Variation

Introduced in October 1984, the *Country Church* underwent colour changes shortly after initial production. Of the 500 pieces produced, the majority of models are in the Second Varaition.

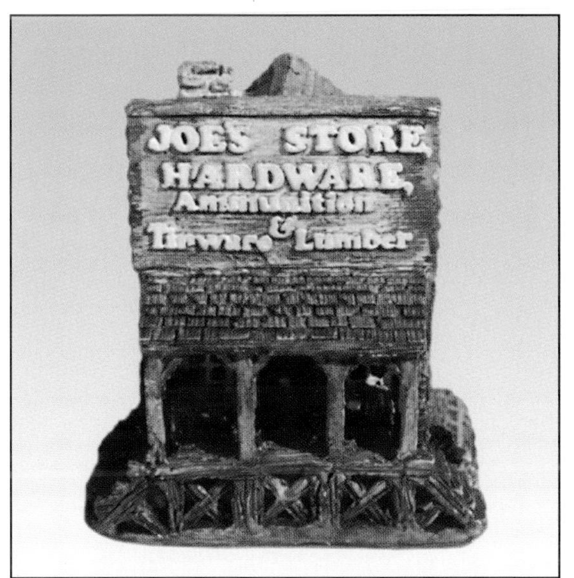

General Store: Approximately 50 of the 150 pieces produced of *General Store* feature red, diagonal lettering rather than white, horizontal lettering.

Grist Mill: A lack of popularity at the time of production resulted in only 150 pieces of this model being made. Today, this model is quite rare.

AMERICAN COLLECTION

Lighthouse: Introduced in 1984, only 200 pieces of this model were produced. It was sold exclusively in the USA.

Wallace Station: Based on the "Whistle Stations" along the Union and Pacific Railway Lines, only 150 models were produced.

San Francisco House, First Variation

San Francisco House, Second Variation

Introduced in October 1984, two colourways of this model exist: the first has pink walls, white windows and a brown door, while the second has yellow walls, white windows and a blue door.

AN AMERICAN JOURNEY by Ray Day

Daydreams: This model was inspired by the Smith Bridge, c.1887, spanning the Flatrock River in Rush County, Indiana.

Dog Days of Summer: Introduced in 1997, *Dog Days of Summer* was modelled from a Kirbyville, Missouri, farm.

Lace House: This piece was modelled after an American Gothic style home in Black Hawk, Colorado.

Morning has Broken: Babcock State Park, West Virginia, is home to this building, created in 1976 from a variety of old mills.

THE COCA COLA™ COLLECTION by Ray Day

"A Cherry Coke - Just the Prescription" ™: Introduced in 1995, this model is based on a shop in Silver Plume, Colorado.

Dixie Bottling Company™: The first bottling facility for Coca Cola, this building was constructed on Edgewood Avenue, Atlanta in 1890.

'Fill'er Up and Check the Oil™: Typical of pre-World War II service stations built along American highways, this model was introduced in 1995.

Hook, Line and Sinker™ : Based on a typical 1930s/40s bait and tackle shop in the rural Midwest, *Hook, Line and Sinker* was exclusive to North America.

THE COCA COLA™ COLLECTION by Ray Day

The Lunch Line™: Introduced in 1997, *The Lunch Line* depicts a renovated old train carriage that has been converted into a small café/snack bar.

"Milk for Mom and A Coke For Me"™: This model was inspired by a turn-of-the-century building in New Albany, Indiana.

"Mmm... Just Like Home"™: Based on the typical rural restaurant found in small American towns, *"Mmm ... Just Like Home* was released in 1997.

Santa's Corner™: Made under license from the Coca Cola™ Company, *Santa's Corner* was introduced as a limited edition of 19,960 in 1996.

THE COCA COLA™ COLLECTION by Ray Day

Saturday Night Jive™: Based on an old mill in Silver Creek, Indiana, this model was introduced in 1997.

"They Don't Make 'em Like They Used To"™: Available only in North America, this model was inspired by a Federal-style brick structure in New England

"We've Got It ... (Or They Don't Make It)" ™: Designed for the North American market, this piece is reminiscent of country stores built in the late 1920s.

"Wet Your Whistle"™: This model was based on a hundred-year-old water tower, which was once used to fill steam engines.

7 ST. ANDREWS SQUARE

Code No.:	Unknown
Size:	2 ¼", 5.7 cm
Backstamp:	D
Introduced:	1985-1986
Location:	Culross, Fife
Series:	Scottish
Can.	$250.00
U.S.	$185.00
U.K.	£125.00

SHADES OF SUMMER

Code No.:	L2125
Size:	4 ½", 11.9 cm
Backstamp:	Q-2
Introduced:	1998-1998
Location:	Patrixbourne, Kent
Series:	Anniversary Editions
Can.	$200.00
U.S.	$135.00
U.K.	£ 85.00

SHAKESPEARE'S BIRTHPLACE

Code No.:	L2214
Size:	3 ¼", 8.3 cm
Backstamp:	Q-2
Introduced:	1998 to the present
Location:	Stratford-upon-Avon
Series:	Britain's Heritage™
Can.	$80.00
U.S.	$50.00
U.K.	£19.95

SHAVE AND A HAIRCUT

Code No.:	655
Size:	3", 7.5 cm
Backstamp:	L
Introduced:	1993-1997
Location:	Wytopitloch, Maine
Series:	American Landmarks
Can.	$125.00
U.S.	$ 85.00
U.K.	£ 55.00

SHIP INN

Code No.:	Unknown
Size:	5 ¾", 14.6 cm
Backstamp:	G
Introduced:	1988-1992
Location:	York
Series:	English: Northern
Can.	$275.00
U.S.	$200.00
U.K.	£135.00

"SHORT BACK AND SIDES?"

Code No.:	L2200
Size:	4 ¾", 12.1 cm
Backstamp:	Q-2
Introduced:	1998-1999
Series:	Moments in Time
Can.	$150.00
U.S.	$ 90.00
U.K.	£ 45.00

SHRINE OF DEMOCRACY (MOUNT RUSHMORE)

Code No.: 723193
Size: 6 ¼" x 4 ½" x 3 ¾", 15.9 x 11.9 x 9.5 cm
Backstamp: R
Introduced: 2000 to the present
Series: America's National Treasures

Can. N/A
U.S. $50.00
U.K. N/A

SHROPSHIRE COTTAGE

Code No.: Unknown
Size: 3 ¼", 8.3 cm
Backstamp: L
Introduced: 1993-1994
Series: Paint Your Own

Can. $60.00
U.S. $40.00
U.K. £25.00

Note: Prices refer to unpainted models, which are more valuable.

"SIGN OF GOOD TASTE"™

Code No.: L2220
Size: 2 ½", 6.4 cm
Backstamp: Q-2
Introduced: 1998 to the present
Series: America's Favourites

Can. N/A
U.S. $37.50
U.K. N/A

SILENT NIGHT

Code No.: L2318
Size: 3", 7.6 cm
Backstamp: R
Introduced: 2000-2000
Series: Christmas Annual Ornament

Can. $55.00
U.S. $35.00
U.K. £15.50

SILVER BELLS

Code No.: L2067
Size: 2", 5.0 cm
Backstamp: P-1
Introduced: 1997-2000
Location: Castle Combe, Wiltshire
Series: English

Can. $40.00
U.S. $25.00
U.K. £ 9.95

SIMPLY AMISH

Code No.: 149
Size: 4", 10.1 cm
Backstamp: L
Introduced: 1993-1998
Location: Harrison County, Indiana
Series: American Landmarks

Can. $135.00
U.S. $ 95.00
U.K. £ 60.00

16.9 CENTS PER GALLON

Code No.: 628
Size: 3", 7.6 cm
Backstamp: K-1
Introduced: 1992-1999
Location: New Russia, New York
Series: American Landmarks

Can. $125.00
U.S. $ 85.00
U.K. £ 55.00

SMALL TOWN LIBRARY

Code No.: 557
Size: 4", 10.1 cm
Backstamp: K-1
Introduced: 1992-1995
Location: Rugby, Tennessee
Series: American Landmarks

Can. $175.00
U.S. $125.00
U.K. £ 80.00

THE SMALLEST INN

Code No.: 049
Size: 2 ¼", 5.7 cm
Backstamp: G
Introduced: 1988-1991
Location: Dorset
Series: English: South-West

Can. $85.00
U.S. $60.00
U.K. £40.00

SMUGGLERS' REST

Code No.: L2331
Size: 3 ½", 8.9 cm
Backstamp: R
Introduced: 2000 to the present
Series: English

Can. $95.00
U.S. $65.00
U.K. £25.95

SNOWDON LODGE

Code No.: 678
Size: 4 ¼", 10.8 cm
Backstamp: M
Introduced: 1994-1994
Location: Garreg, Wales
Series: Christmas Lodge

Can. $200.00
U.S. $135.00
U.K. £ 85.00

SORE PAWS

Code No.: L2022
Size: 3 ¾", 9.5 cm
Backstamp: O-2
Introduced: 1996 to the present
Location: Middleham, Yorkshire
Series: English: Northern

Can. $120.00
U.S. $ 70.00
U.K. £ 35.95

THE SPINDLES

Code No.:	L2010
Size:	3", 7.6 cm
Backstamp:	O-2
Introduced:	1996-1999
Location:	Kilburn, Yorkshire
Series:	English: Northern
Can.	$100.00
U.S.	$ 70.00
U.K.	£ 45.00

THE SPINNEY

Code No.:	Unknown
Size:	2 ½", 6 4 cm
Backstamp:	L
Introduced:	1993-1994
Series:	Collectors Club
Can.	$60.00
U.S.	$40.00
U.K.	£25.00

SPRING BANK

Code No.:	Unknown
Size:	2 ½", 6.4 cm
Backstamp:	E
Introduced:	1986-1991
Location:	Lyme Regis, Dorset
Series:	English: South-West
Can.	$70.00
U.S.	$50.00
U.K.	£30.00

SPRING GATE COTTAGE

Code No.:	696
Size:	4", 10.1 cm
Backstamp:	M
Introduced:	1994-1997
Location:	Luccombe, Somerset
Series:	English: South-West
Can.	$100.00
U.S.	$ 75.00
U.K.	£ 45.00

SPRING GLORY

Code No.:	741
Size:	3 ½", 8.9 cm
Backstamp:	N-1
Introduced:	1995-1997
Varieties:	Autumn Hues, Summer Impressions, Winter's Wonder
Location:	Wiltshire
Series:	Year in English Garden
Can.	$100.00
U.S.	$ 70.00
U.K.	£ 45.00

SPRING VICTORIAN

Code No.:	684
Size:	3 ¾", 9.5 cm
Backstamp:	M
Introduced:	1994-1998
Location:	Georgetown, Colorado
Series:	American Landmarks
Can.	$225.00
U.S.	$165.00
U.K.	£100.00

ST. COLUMBA'S SCHOOL

Code No.:	465
Size:	2 ½", 6.4 cm
Backstamp:	H-1
Introduced:	1989-1996
Location:	Coony, Donegal
Series:	Irish
Can.	$60.00
U.S.	$40.00
U.K.	£25.00

ST. GOVAN'S CHAPEL

Code No.:	637
Size:	2 ½", 6.0 cm
Backstamp:	K-1
Introduced:	1992-2000
Location:	St. Govan's Head, Pembrokeshire
Series:	Welsh
Can.	$70.00
U.S.	$50.00
U.K.	£19.95

ST. JOHN THE BAPTIST

Code No.:	006
Size:	4", 10.1 cm
Backstamp:	O-2
Introduced:	1996-1998
Location:	North Yorkshire
Series:	English: Northern
Can.	$85.00
U.S.	$60.00
U.K.	£35.00

ST. JOSEPH'S CHURCH

Code No.:	641
Size:	3 ½", 8.9 cm
Backstamp:	L
Introduced:	1993-1997
Series:	Christmas
Can.	$70.00
U.S.	$45.00
U.K.	£30.00

ST. JOSEPH'S SCHOOL

Code No.:	675
Size:	2 ¾", 7.0 cm
Backstamp:	M
Introduced:	1994-1997
Location:	Eastcombe, Gloucestershire
Series:	Christmas
Can.	$50.00
U.S.	$35.00
U.K.	£20.00

ST. KEVIN'S CHURCH

Code No.:	460
Size:	4", 10.1 cm
Backstamp:	H-1
Introduced:	1989-1996
Location:	Glen Dalough Valley, County Wicklow
Series:	Irish
Can.	$70.00
U.S.	$50.00
U.K.	£30.00

ST. LAWRENCE CHURCH
First Version - 5″

Code No.:	564
Size:	5″, 12.7 cm
Backstamp:	H-1
Introduced:	1989-1998
Location:	Crosby Ravensworth, Cumbria
Series:	English: Northern
Can.	$100.00
U.S.	$ 75.00
U.K.	£ 45.00

ST. LAWRENCE CHURCH
Second Version - 1 ½″

Code No.:	Unknown
Size:	1 ½", 3.9 cm
Backstamp:	None
Introduced:	1997-1999
Location:	Crosby Ravensworth, Cumbria
Series:	Dream Cottage Miniatures
Can.	$45.00
U.S.	$30.00
U.K.	£20.00

ST. MARK'S CHURCH

Code No.:	164
Size:	3 ¾″, 9.5 cm
Backstamp:	G
Introduced:	1988-1991
Series:	English: Midlands
Can.	$140.00
U.S.	$100.00
U.K.	£ 65.00

ST. MARY'S CHURCH
Style One

Code No.:	Unknown
Size:	3 ¾″, 9.5 cm
Backstamp:	D
Introduced:	1985-1988
Series:	English: Midlands
Can.	$175.00
U.S.	$125.00
U.K.	£ 80.00

ST. MARY'S CHURCH
Style Two

Code No.:	Unknown
Size:	6″, 15.0 cm
Backstamp:	M
Introduced:	1994 in a limited edition of 5,000
Location:	Yorkshire
Series:	Studley Royal
Can.	$165.00
U.S.	$115.00
U.K.	£ 70.00

ST. NICHOLAS CHURCH

Code No.:	Unknown
Size:	4″, 10.1 cm
Backstamp:	H-1
Introduced:	1989-1990
Location:	Penrith
Series:	Christmas Specials
Can.	$225.00
U.S.	$150.00
U.K.	£ 95.00

ST. PATRICK'S CHURCH

Code No.:	470
Size:	6", 15.0 cm
Backstamp:	H-1
Introduced:	1989-1993
Location:	County Donegal, Ireland
Series:	Irish
Can.	$250.00
U.S.	$175.00
U.K.	£110.00

ST. PETER'S COVE

Code No.:	Unknown
Size:	8", 20.3 cm
Backstamp:	Special limited edition
Introduced:	1989 in a limited edition of 3,000
Series:	English: South-East
Can.	$2,000.00
U.S.	$1,500.00
U.K.	£ 950.00

ST. STEPHEN'S CHURCH

Code No.:	849
Size:	5 ½", 14.0 cm
Backstamp:	O-2
Introduced:	1996-1996
Location:	Higham, Suffolk
Series:	Christmas
Can.	$100.00
U.S.	$ 75.00
U.K.	£ 45.00

THE STAR INN

Code No.:	L2319
Size:	4 ¼", 10.8 cm
Backstamp:	R
Introduced:	2000-2000
Series:	Special Editions
Can.	$220.00
U.S.	$150.00
U.K.	£ 59.95

STARGAZER'S COTTAGE

Code No.:	L2244
Size:	4 ¼", 10.8 cm
Backstamp:	R
Introduced:	1999-2000
Series:	Millennium
Can.	$160.00
U.S.	$ 90.00
U.K.	£ 39.95

STARS AND STRIPES FOREVER

Code No.:	L2164
Size:	3 ¾", 9.5 cm
Backstamp:	Unknown
Introduced:	1998 to the present
Location:	Philadelphia, Pennsylvania
Series:	Allegiance
Can.	N/A
U.S.	$75.00
U.K.	£35.95

STOCKLEBECK MILL

Code No.: 150
Size: 4 ¾", 12.1 cm
Backstamp: L
Introduced: 1993-1999
Location: Cumbria
Series: English: Northern

Can. $275.00
U.S. $185.00
U.K. £125.00

STOCKWELL TENEMENT

Code No.: 480
Size: 4 ¼", 10.8 cm
Backstamp: H-1
Introduced: 1989-1996
Series: Scottish

Can. $90.00
U.S. $60.00
U.K. £40.00

STOKESAY

Code No.: 685
Size: 3 ½", 8.9 cm
Backstamp: M
Introduced: 1994-1998
Location: Shropshire
Series: Historic Castles of Britain

Can. $100.00
U.S. $ 75.00
U.K. £ 45.00

Photograph not available at press time.

See next image for shape outline.

Photograph not available at press time.

See previous image for shape outline.

STONE COTTAGE

First Version (10 tiles, no lintel)

Code No.: Unknown
Size: 3 ¾", 9.5 cm
Backstamp: None
Introduced: 1982-1982
Series: English: South-East

Can. $2,000.00
U.S. $1,475.00
U.K. £ 900.00

STONE COTTAGE

Second Version (10 tiles, single lintel)

Code No.: Unknown
Size: 3 ¾", 9.5 cm
Backstamp: A-1, None
Introduced: 1982-1982
Series: English: South-East

Can. $1,000.00
U.S. $ 750.00
U.K. £ 475.00

STONE COTTAGE

Third Version (5 tiles, double lintel)

Code No.: Unknown
Size: 3 ½", 8.9 cm
Backstamp: A-1, A-2
Introduced: 1982-1983
Series: English: South-East

Can. $575.00
U.S. $400.00
U.K. £250.00

STONE COTTAGE

Fouth Version (4 tiles, single lintel)

Code No.:	Unknown
Size:	3 ¾", 9.5 cm
Backstamp:	C
Introduced:	1983-1986
Series:	English: South-East
Can.	$500.00
U.S.	$325.00
U.K.	£200.00

STONE COTTAGE

Fifth Version (4 roof tiles, higher chimney pots)

Code No.:	Unknown
Size:	4", 10.1 cm
Backstamp:	C
Introduced:	1986-1986
Series:	English: South-East
Can.	$800.00
U.S.	$550.00
U.K.	£350.00

THE STONEMASON

Code No.:	L2140
Size:	3 ¾", 9.5 cm
Backstamp:	Q-2
Introduced:	1998-1999
Location:	Sandy Lane, Wiltshire
Series:	English
Can.	$140.00
U.S.	$100.00
U.K.	£ 65.00

Photograph not available at press time.

See next image for shape outline.

STONEYBECK

First Variation (Light blue windows)

Code No.:	146A
Size:	2 ¾", 7.0 cm
Backstamp:	F
Introduced:	1987-1992
Location:	Lake District
Series:	English: Northern
Can.	$70.00
U.S.	$50.00
U.K.	£30.00

STONEYBECK

Second Variation (Buff windows)

Code No.:	146B
Size:	2 ¾", 7.0 cm
Backstamp:	F
Introduced:	1987-1992
Location:	Lake District
Series:	English: Northern
Can.	$70.00
U.S.	$50.00
U.K.	£30.00

STRADLING PRIORY

Code No.:	153
Size:	4 ¼", 10.8 cm
Backstamp:	L
Introduced:	1993-1997
Location:	Glastonbury, Somerset
Series:	English: South-West
Can.	$100.00
U.S.	$ 75.00
U.K.	£ 45.00

STRANDVOGTHAUS

Code No.: 263
Size: 2 ¾", 7.0 cm
Backstamp: I-1
Introduced: 1992-1998
Location: Sylt, Germany
Series: German

Can. $110.00
U.S. $ 80.00
U.K. £ 50.00

STRAWBERRY COTTAGE

Code No.: 505
Size: 2 ½", 6.4 cm
Backstamp: I-1
Introduced: 1990-1998
Location: Steyning, East Sussex
Series: English: South-East

Can. $50.00
U.S. $35.00
U.K. £20.00

STRAWBERRY TEAS

Code No.: L2158
Size: 3 ¾", 9.5 cm
Backstamp: P-2
Introduced: 1998 to the present
Location: Dunnose, Isle of Wight
Series: English Tea Rooms

Can. $190.00
U.S. $100.00
U.K. £ 49.95

STREET SCENE NO.1

Code No.: Unknown
Size: 6-7", 15.0-17.8 cm
Backstamp: F
Introduced: 1987-1987
Series: Street Scene

Can. $140.00
U.S. $100.00
U.K. £ 65.00

STREET SCENE NO.2

Code No.: Unknown
Size: 6-7", 15.0-17.8 cm
Backstamp: F
Introduced: 1987-1987
Series: Street Scene

Can. $140.00
U.S. $100.00
U.K. £ 65.00

STREET SCENE NO.3

Code No.: Unknown
Size: 6-7", 15.0-17.8 cm
Backstamp: F
Introduced: 1987-1987
Series: Street Scene

Can. $140.00
U.S. $100.00
U.K. £ 65.00

STREET SCENE NO.4

Code No.: Unknown
Size: 6-7", 15.0-17.8 cm
Backstamp: F
Introduced: 1987-1987
Series: Street Scene

Can. $140.00
U.S. $100.00
U.K. £ 65.00

STREET SCENE NO.5

Code No.: Unknown
Size: 6-7", 15.0-17.8 cm
Backstamp: F
Introduced: 1987-1987
Series: Street Scene

Can. $140.00
U.S. $100.00
U.K. £ 65.00

STREET SCENE NO.6

Code No.: Unknown
Size: 6-7", 15.0-17.8 cm
Backstamp: F
Introduced: 1987-1987
Series: Street Scene

Can. $140.00
U.S. $100.00
U.K. £ 65.00

STREET SCENE NO.7

Code No.: Unknown
Size: 6-7", 15.0-17.8 cm
Backstamp: F
Introduced: 1987-1987
Series: Street Scene

Can. $140.00
U.S. $100.00
U.K. £ 65.00

STREET SCENE NO.8

Code No.: Unknown
Size: 6-7", 15.0-17.8 cm
Backstamp: F
Introduced: 1987-1987
Series: Street Scene

Can. $140.00
U.S. $100.00
U.K. £ 65.00

STREET SCENE NO.9

Code No.: Unknown
Size: 6-7", 15.0-17.8 cm
Backstamp: F
Introduced: 1987-1987
Series: Street Scene

Can. $140.00
U.S. $100.00
U.K. £ 65.00

STREET SCENE NO.10

Code No.: Unknown
Size: 6-7", 15.0-17.8 cm
Backstamp: F
Introduced: 1987-1987
Series: Street Scene

Can. $140.00
U.S. $100.00
U.K. £ 65.00

SUFFOLK COTTAGE

Code No.: 761
Size: 3", 7.6 cm
Backstamp: N-1
Introduced: 1995 to the present
Series: Paint Your Own

Can. $45.00
U.S. $30.00
U.K. £20.00

Note: Prices refer to unpainted models, which are more valuable.

SUFFOLK PINKS

Code No.: L2135
Size: 2 ½", 6.4 cm
Backstamp: Q-2
Introduced: 1998 to the present
Series: Paint Your Own

Can. N/A
U.S. $17.50
U.K. £ 9.00

Note: Prices refer to unpainted models, which are more valuable.

SULGRAVE MANOR

Code No.: 497
Size: 3 ¾", 9 5 cm
Backstamp: H-1
Introduced: 1990-1992
Location: Northamptonshire
Series: English: Midlands

Can. $175.00
U.S. $125.00
U.K. £ 80.00

SUMMER DAYS

Code No.: L2059
Size: 4", 10.1 cm
Backstamp: P-1
Introduced: 1997-1997
Location: Cuddington, Buckinghamshire
Series: Anniversary Editions

Can. $175.00
U.S. $130.00
U.K. £ 80.00

SUMMER HAZE

First Version - 4"

Code No.: 074
Size: 4", 10.1 cm
Backstamp: F
Introduced: 1987-1993
Location: Oxfordshire
Series: English: Midlands

Can. $135.00
U.S. $ 95.00
U.K. £ 60.00

SUMMER HAZE
Second Version - 1 ¼"

Code No.:	Unknown
Size:	1 ¼", 3.1 cm
Backstamp:	None
Introduced:	1997-1999
Location:	Oxfordshire
Series:	Dream Cottage Miniatures
Can.	$45.00
U.S.	$30.00
U.K.	£20.00

SUMMER IMPRESSIONS

Code No.:	742
Size:	3 ½", 8.9 cm
Backstamp:	N-1
Introduced:	1995-1997
Varieties:	Autumn Hues, Spring Glory, Winter's Wonder
Location:	Wiltshire
Series:	Year in English Garden
Can.	$100.00
U.S.	$ 75.00
U.K.	£ 45.00

SUNNYSIDE

Code No.:	693
Size:	2 ½", 6.4 cm
Backstamp:	M
Introduced:	1994-1997
Location:	Selbourne, Hampshire
Series:	English: South-East
Can.	$50.00
U.S.	$35.00
U.K.	£20.00

SUSSEX MILL
First Version (28 windows, cutaway base)

Code No.:	Unknown
Size:	2 ¼", 5.7 cm
Backstamp:	A-1, A-2
Introduced:	1982-1984
Location:	Sussex
Series:	English: South-East
Can.	$1,000.00
U.S.	$ 725.00
U.K.	£ 475.00

SUSSEX MILL
Second Version (14 windows, circular base)

Code No.:	Unknown
Size:	2 ½", 6.4 cm
Backstamp:	C
Introduced:	1984-1986
Location:	Sussex
Series:	English: South-East
Can.	$500.00
U.S.	$350.00
U.K.	£225.00

SWALEDALE TEAS

Code No.:	L2015
Size:	3 ½", 8.9 cm
Backstamp:	O-2
Introduced:	1996-1999
Location:	Muker, North Yorkshire
Series:	English Tea Rooms
Can.	$100.00
U.S.	$ 75.00
U.K.	£ 45.00

SWAN INN

Code No.:	Unknown
Size:	5", 12.7 cm
Backstamp:	G
Introduced:	1988-1992
Location:	Midhurst, Sussex
Series:	English: South-East
Can.	$200.00
U.S.	$135.00
U.K.	£ 85.00

SWEET BRIAR COTTAGE
First Version - 4 ½"

Code No.:	Unknown
Size:	4 ½", 11.9 cm
Backstamp:	I-2
Introduced:	1990-1995
Location:	Bristol
Series:	1. Blaise Hamlet 2. English: South-West
Can.	$140.00
U.S.	$100.00
U.K.	£ 65.00

SWEET BRIAR COTTAGE
Second Version - 2 ½"

Code No.:	526
Size:	2 ½", 6.4 cm
Backstamp:	L
Introduced:	1993-1995
Location:	Bristol
Series:	Classics
Can.	$100.00
U.S.	$ 75.00
U.K.	£ 45.00

SWEET PEA COT

Code No.:	692
Size:	2 ½", 6.4 cm
Backstamp:	M
Introduced:	1994-1997
Location:	Selworthy, Somerset
Series:	English: South-West
Can.	$45.00
U.S.	$30.00
U.K.	£20.00

SWEET WILLIAM

Code No.:	L2046
Size:	2 ¼", 5.7 cm
Backstamp:	P-1
Introduced:	1997-1998
Location:	Stagsden, Bedfordshire
Series:	English
Can.	$45.00
U.S.	$30.00
U.K.	£20.00

SWEETS AND TREATS

Code No.:	L2315
Size:	4", 10.1 cm
Backstamp:	R
Introduced:	2000-2000
Series:	Anniversary Cottage
Can.	$220.00
U.S.	$160.00
U.K.	£ 59.95

SWIFT HOLLOW

Code No.:	165
Size:	3 ¼", 8.3 cm
Backstamp:	G
Introduced:	1988-1990
Location:	Hampshire
Series:	English: South-East
Can.	$100.00
U.S.	$ 70.00
U.K.	£ 45.00

SYON CONSERVATORY

Code No.:	Unknown
Size:	Unknown
Backstamp:	R
Introduced:	2000
Series:	Special Edition
Can.	N/A
U.S.	N/A
U.K.	£34.95

TABITHA TWITCHET'S SHOP™

Code No.:	L2271
Size:	3", 7.6 cm
Backstamp:	R
Introduced:	1999 to the present
Series:	Beatrix Potter™
Can.	N/A
U.S.	$65.00
U.K.	£28.50

THE TAILOR

Code No.:	L2054
Size:	4", 10.1 cm
Backstamp:	P-1
Introduced:	1997-1999
Location:	Cumbria
Series:	Victorian Shops
Can.	$110.00
U.S.	$ 80.00
U.K.	£ 50.00

TANGLEWOOD LODGE

Code No.:	076
Size:	4 ½", 11.9 cm
Backstamp:	H-1
Introduced:	1989-1992
Location:	Cotswolds
Series:	English: South-East
Can.	$150.00
U.S.	$110.00
U.K.	£ 70.00

TANNERS COTTAGE

First Variation
(Dark brown door, foliage)

Code No.:	Unknown
Size:	2", 5.0 cm
Backstamp:	F
Introduced:	1987-1990
Location:	Bedford
Series:	English: Midlands
Can.	$100.00
U.S.	$ 75.00
U.K.	£ 45.00

TANNERS COTTAGE

Second Variation
(Light brown door, foliage)

Code No.: Unknown
Size: 2", 5.0 cm
Backstamp: F
Introduced: 1990-1992
Location: Bedford
Series: English: Midlands

Can. $60.00
U.S. $45.00
U.K. £30.00

TARNSIDE

Code No: L2192
Size: 3 ¼", 8.3 cm
Backstamp: Q-2
Introduced: 1998-2000
Series: Bed and Breakfast

Can. N/A
U.S. $85.00
U.K. £30.00

TEA CADDY COTTAGE

Code No.: 674
Size: 3 ½", 8.9cm
Backstamp: M
Introduced: 1994-1998
Location: Higham
Series: English: South-East

Can. $70.00
U.S. $50.00
U.K. £30.00

TEMPLE BAR FOLLY

Code No.: L2297
Size: 3", 7.6 cm
Backstamp: R
Introduced: 1999 to the present
Series: English

Can. N/A
U.S. $55.00
U.K. £19.95

THE TEMPLE OF PIETY

Code No.: Unknown
Size: 3", 7.6 cm
Backstamp: M
Introduced: 1994 in a limited edition of 5,000
Location: Ripon, Yorkshire
Series: Studley Royal

Can. $100.00
U.S. $ 75.00
U.K. £ 45.00

THATCHER'S REST

Code No.: Unknown
Size: 3 ½", 8.9 cm
Backstamp: B
Introduced: 1983-1988
Location: Meon Valley, Hampshire
Series: English: South-East

Can. $400.00
U.S. $275.00
U.K. £175.00

"THEY DON'T MAKE 'EM LIKE THEY USED TO"™

Code No.:	L2167
Size:	3 ¼", 8.3 cm
Backstamp:	Unknown
Introduced:	1998-2000
Location:	New England
Series:	Coca-Cola™ Country
Can.	$100.00
U.S.	$ 70.00
U.K.	£ 45.00

THIMBLE COTTAGE

Code No.:	765
Size:	2 ½", 6.4 cm
Backstamp:	N-1
Introduced:	1995-1996
Location:	Cornwall
Series:	Collectors Club
Can.	$60.00
U.S.	$40.00
U.K.	£25.00

"THIS BUD'S FOR YOU"™

Code No.:	L2217
Size:	3 ½", 8.9 cm
Backstamp:	Q-2
Introduced:	1998 to the present
Series:	America's Favourites
Can.	N/A
U.S.	$37.50
U.K.	N/A

THOOR BALLYLEE

Code No.:	Unknown
Size:	4", 10.1 cm
Backstamp:	H-1
Introduced:	1989-1992
Location:	Galway, Ireland
Series:	Irish
Can.	$175.00
U.S.	$125.00
U.K.	£ 80.00

THE THORNERY

Code No.:	Unknown
Size:	4", 10.1 cm
Backstamp:	Q-2
Introduced:	1998-1998
Series:	Special Edition
Can.	$200.00
U.S.	$150.00
U.K.	£ 95.00

THREE FEATHERS

First Variation (White plastic sign)

Code No.:	Unknown
Size:	4 ¾", 12.1 cm
Backstamp:	E
Introduced:	1986-1989
Location:	Cambridgeshire
Series:	English: South-East
Can.	$450.00
U.S.	$300.00
U.K.	£200.00

THREE FEATHERS
Second Variation (Black metal sign)

Code No.:	Unknown
Size:	4 ¾", 12.1 cm
Backstamp:	E
Introduced:	1986-1989
Location:	Cambridgeshire
Series:	English: South-East
Can.	$300.00
U.S.	$200.00
U.K.	£125.00

TILLERS GREEN

Code No.:	431
Size:	2 ¾", 7.0 cm
Backstamp:	J
Introduced:	1991-1995
Location:	Gloucestershire
Series:	English: Midlands
Can.	$70.00
U.S.	$50.00
U.K.	£30.00

"TIME GENTLEMEN PLEASE!"

Code No.:	L2199
Size:	4 ¼", 11.9 cm
Backstamp:	Q-2
Introduced:	1998-1999
Series:	Moments in Time
Can.	$150.00
U.S.	$ 90.00
U.K.	£ 45.00

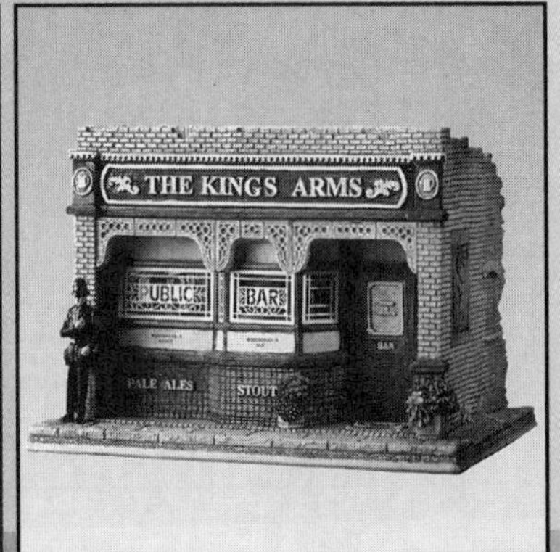

TINTAGEL

Code No.:	Unknown
Size:	2 ¾", 7.0 cm
Backstamp:	C
Introduced:	1984-1988
Varieties:	The Old Post Office
Location:	Tintagel, Cornwall
Series:	English: South-West
Can.	$275.00
U.S.	$190.00
U.K.	£125.00

TIRED TIMBERS

Code No.:	724
Size:	3", 7.6 cm
Backstamp:	M
Introduced:	1994-1997
Location:	Preston-on-Stour, Warwickshire
Series:	English: Midlands
Can.	$70.00
U.S.	$50.00
U.K.	£30.00

TITMOUSE COTTAGE
First Version - 4"

Code No.:	565
Size:	4", 10.1 cm
Backstamp:	H-1
Introduced:	1989-1995
Series:	English: South-West
Can.	$140.00
U.S.	$100.00
U.K.	£ 65.00

TITMOUSE COTTAGE
Second Version - 1 ½"

Code No.:	Unknown
Size:	1 ½", 3.9 cm
Backstamp:	None
Introduced:	1997-1999
Series:	Dream Cottage Miniatures
Can.	$45.00
U.S.	$30.00
U.K.	£20.00

TITWILLOW COTTAGE

Code No.:	646
Size:	2 ½", 6.4 cm
Backstamp:	L
Introduced:	1993-1997
Location:	Eardisley, Herefordshire
Series:	English: Midlands
Can.	$50.00
U.S.	$35.00
U.K.	£25.00

TO GRANDMOTHER'S HOUSE WE GO

Code No.:	L2066
Size:	4 ½", 11.9 cm
Backstamp:	P-1
Introduced:	1997-1997
Location:	Corydon, Massachucetts
Series:	Christmas in America
Can.	$175.00
U.S.	$125.00
U.K.	£ 80.00

TO HAVE AND TO HOLD

Code No.:	L2226
Size:	3 ½", 8.9 cm
Backstamp:	R
Introduced:	1999 to the present
Series:	English
Can.	$100.00
U.S.	$ 60.00
U.K.	£ 25.95

THE TOADSTOOL

Code No.:	L2322
Size:	2 ½", 6.4 cm
Backstamp:	R
Introduced:	2000 to the present
Series:	English
Can.	$35.00
U.S.	$25.00
U.K.	£ 9.95

TOLL HOUSE
First Version (Narrow chimney base)

Code No.:	Unknown
Size:	2 ¼", 5.7 cm
Backstamp:	A-1, A2
Introduced:	1983-1983
Location:	Hertfordshire
Series:	English: South-East
Can.	$400.00
U.S.	$275.00
U.K.	£175.00

TOLL HOUSE

Second Version (Wide chimney base)

Code No.:	Unknown
Size:	2 ¼", 5.7 cm
Backstamp:	B
Introduced:	1983-1983
Location:	Hertfordshire
Series:	English: South-East
Can.	$250.00
U.S.	$175.00
U.K.	£110.00

TOWER BANK ARMS™

Code No.:	L2270
Size:	3 ½", 8.9 cm
Backstamp:	R
Introduced:	1999 to the present
Series:	Beatrix Potter™
Can.	N/A
U.S.	$65.00
U.K.	£28.50

TOWER BRIDGE

Code No.:	L2213
Size:	4 ¾", 12.2 cm
Backstamp:	Q-2
Introduced:	1998 to the present
Location:	London
Series:	Britain's Heritage™
Can.	$100.00
U.S.	$ 55.00
U.K.	£ 29.95

TOWER OF LONDON

Code No.:	L2210
Size:	4", 10.1 cm
Backstamp:	Q-2
Introduced:	1998 to the present
Location:	London
Series:	Britain's Heritage™
Can.	$80.00
U.S.	$50.00
U.K.	£25.95

THE TOY SHOP

First Version - 4"

Code No.:	690
Size:	4", 10.1 cm
Backstamp:	M
Introduced:	1994-1999
Series:	Village Shops
Can.	$100.00
U.S.	$ 70.00
U.K.	£ 45.00

THE TOY SHOP

Second Version - 1 ½"

Code No.:	Unknown
Size:	1 ½", 3.9 cm
Backstamp:	None
Introduced:	1997-1999
Series:	Dream Cottage Miniatures
Can.	$45.00
U.S.	$30.00
U.K.	£20.00

TRANQUIL TREASURE

Code No.: L2196
Size: 5 ¼", 13.3 cm
Backstamp: Q-2
Introduced: 1998 to the present
Series: Secret Gardens™

Can. $130.00
U.S. $ 80.00
U.K. £ 35.95

TRANQUILITY

Code No.: Unknown
Size: 5 ½", 14.0 cm
Backstamp: N-1
Introduced: 1995 in a limited edition of 2,500
Series: Garden

Can. $700.00
U.S. $500.00
U.K. £325.00

TROUTBECK FARM

First Version (Resin)

Code No.: Unknown
Size: 3 ½", 8.9 cm
Backstamp: Unknown
Introduced: 1983-1985
Location: Lake District
Series: English: Northern

Can.
U.S. Very Rare
U.K.

TROUTBECK FARM

Second Version (Crystacal)

Code No.: Unknown
Size: 3 ½", 8.9 cm
Backstamp: B
Introduced: 1983-1985
Location: Lake District
Series: English: Northern

Can. $850.00
U.S. $600.00
U.K. £375.00

TROUTBECK FARM

Third Version (Amorphite)

Code No.: Unknown
Size: 3 ½", 8.9 cm
Backstamp: B, C
Introduced: 1985-1987
Location: Lake District
Series: English: Northern

Can. $575.00
U.S. $400.00
U.K. £250.00

"TRUST YOUR CAR TO THE STAR"™

Code No.: L2218
Size: 3", 7.6 cm
Backstamp: Q-2
Introduced: 1998 to the present
Series: America's Favourites

Can. N/A
U.S. $37.50
U.K. N/A

TUCK SHOP
First Version (10 Window Panes)

Code No.:	Unknown
Size:	3 ½", 8.9 cm
Backstamp:	A-1, B
Introduced:	1983-1983
Location:	Lake District
Series:	English: Northern
Can.	$1,300.00
U.S.	$1,000.00
U.K.	£ 650.00

TUCK SHOP
Second Version (20 Window Panes)

Code No.:	Unknown
Size:	3 ½", 8.9 cm
Backstamp:	C
Introduced:	1983-1986
Location:	Lake District
Series:	English: Northern
Can.	$700.00
U.S.	$500.00
U.K.	£325.00

TUDOR COURT
First Version, First Variation
(Grey chimney, no retaining wall)

Code No.:	Unknown
Size:	5 ½", 14.0 cm
Backstamp:	E
Introduced:	1986-1989
Location:	Shrewsbury
Series:	English: Midlands
Can.	$550.00
U.S.	$375.00
U.K.	£250.00

Photograph not available at press time.

See previous image for shape outline.

TUDOR COURT
First Version, Second Variation
(Black chimney, no retaining wall)

Code No.:	Unknown
Size:	5 ½", 14.0
Backstamp:	E
Introduced:	1989-1990
Location:	Shrewsbury
Series:	English: Midlands
Can.	$500.00
U.S.	$350.00
U.K.	£225.00

TUDOR COURT
Second Version
(Black chimney, with retaining wall)

Code No.:	Unknown
Size:	5 ½", 14.0
Backstamp:	E
Introduced:	1990-1992
Location:	Shrewsbury
Series:	English: Midlands
Can.	$425.00
U.S.	$300.00
U.K.	£175.00

TUDOR MERCHANT

Code No.:	417
Size:	4 ½", 11.9 cm
Backstamp:	I-2
Introduced:	1991-1997
Location:	Tenby
Series:	Welsh
Can.	$90.00
U.S.	$65.00
U.K.	£40.00

TUPPENNY BUN

Code No.: L2131
Size: 2 ½", 6.4 cm
Backstamp: P-1
Introduced: 1998 to the present
Location: Brigstock, Northamptonshire
Series: English

Can. $65.00
U.S. $35.00
U.K. £17.50

TWO HOOTS

Code No.: 699
Size: 3", 7.6 cm
Backstamp: M
Introduced: 1994-1997
Location: Alresford, Hampshire
Series: English: South-East

Can. $65.00
U.S. $45.00
U.K. £30.00

UGLY HOUSE

Code No.: 416
Size: 2 ½", 6.4 cm
Backstamp: I-2
Introduced: 1991-1999
Location: Betws-y-Coed, Wales
Series: Welsh

Can. $65.00
U.S. $45.00
U.K. £30.00

ULLSWATER BOAT HOUSE

Code No.: L2254
Size: 2 ¼", 5.7 cm
Backstamp: R
Introduced: 1999 to the present
Location: Ullswater
Series: English

Can. $50.00
U.S. $32.00
U.K. £13.50

VANBRUGH LODGE

Code No.: 759
Size: 3", 7.6 cm
Backstamp: N-1
Introduced: 1995-1996
Location: Bourne, Lincolnshire
Series: Special Editions

Can. $110.00
U.S. $ 80.00
U.K. £ 60.00

THE VICARAGE

Code No.: 677
Size: 2 ¾", 7.0 cm
Backstamp: M
Introduced: 1994-1997
Location: Littleworth, Oxfordshire
Series: Christmas

Can. $45.00
U.S. $30.00
U.K. £20.00

VICTORIA COTTAGE
First Version (Thin base)

Code No.: Unknown
Size: 3 ½", 8.9 cm
Backstamp: H-1
Introduced: 1989-1990
Series: English: Northern

Can. $100.00
U.S. $ 75.00
U.K. £ 45.00

VICTORIA COTTAGE
Second Version (Thick base)

Code No.: Unknown
Size: 3 ½", 8.9 cm
Backstamp: H-1
Introduced: 1990-1993
Series: English: Northern

Can. $90.00
U.S. $65.00
U.K. £40.00

VICTORIAN ELEGANCE

Code No.: L2153
Size: 4 ¾", 12.1 cm
Backstamp: P-1
Introduced: 1997-2000
Location: San Francisco, California
Series: An American Journey

Can. N/A
U.S. $130.00
U.K. £ 65.95

Photograph not available at press time.

See previous image for shape outline.

VICTORIAN ROMANCE

Code No.: L2308
Size: 4", 10.1 cm
Backstamp: R
Introduced: 2000 to the present
Location: Niagara-on-the-Lake
Series: Special Editions by Ray Day

Can. $370.00
U.S. $250.00
U.K. £ 99.95

VICTORIANA

Code No.: 555
Size: 6", 15.0 cm
Backstamp: J
Introduced: 1991 in a limited edition of 2,500
Location: Rockport, Maine
Series: American Landmarks

Can. $500.00
U.S. $350.00
U.K. £225.00

VILLAGE SCHOOL

Code No.: 602
Size: 3 ¼", 8.3 cm
Backstamp: J
Introduced: 1991-1996
Location: Sawley, Lancashire
Series: English: Northern

Can. $100.00
U.S. $ 75.00
U.K. £ 45.00

VINE COTTAGE
Style One - 4 ½″

Code No.:	509
Size:	4 ½″, 11.9 cm
Backstamp:	I-2
Introduced:	1990-1995
Location:	Bristol
Series:	1. Blaise Hamlet 2. English: South-West
Can.	$165.00
U.S.	$115.00
U.K.	£ 70.00

VINE COTTAGE
Style Two, First Version - 2 ½″

Code No.:	Unknown
Size:	2 ½″, 6.0 cm
Backstamp:	L
Introduced:	1993-1995
Location:	Bristol
Series:	Classics
Can.	$100.00
U.S.	$ 75.00
U.K.	£ 45.00

VINE COTTAGE
Style Two, Second Version - 1 ½″

Code No.:	Unknown
Size:	1 ½″, 3.9 cm
Backstamp:	None
Introduced:	1997-1999
Location:	Bristol
Series:	Dream Cottage Miniatures
Can.	$45.00
U.S.	$30.00
U.K.	£20.00

WAGTAILS

Code No.:	L2185
Size:	2 ½″, 6.4 cm
Backstamp:	Q-2
Introduced:	1998 to the present
Series:	English
Can.	$65.00
U.S.	$35.00
U.K.	£17.50

WALLACE STATION

Code No.:	Unknown
Size:	2 ½″, 6.4 cm
Backstamp:	C
Introduced:	1984-1985
Series:	American (1st)
Can.	$1,000.00
U.S.	$ 675.00
U.K.	£ 425.00

Note: Only 150 models were produced.

WALKER'S REST

Code No.:	L2193
Size:	3 ¼″, 8.3 cm
Backstamp:	Q-2
Introduced:	1998 to the present
Series:	English
Can.	$120.00
U.S.	$ 85.00
U.K.	£ 29.95

WALTON LODGE

Code No.:	L2044
Size:	3 ¾", 9.5 cm
Backstamp:	P-1
Introduced:	1997-1999
Location:	Hertfordshire
Series:	English
Can.	$90.00
U.S.	$60.00
U.K.	£40.00

THE WARREN

Code No.:	L2137
Size:	3 ½", 8.9 cm
Backstamp:	Q-2
Introduced:	1998 to the present
Series:	Paint Your Own
Can.	N/A
U.S.	$17.50
U.K.	£12.50

WARWICK HALL

First Version
(With Name, 3 Windows)

Code No.:	Unknown
Size:	5 ½", 14.0 cm
Backstamp:	A-1
Introduced:	1983-1983
Location:	Alderley Edge, Cheshire
Series:	English: Northern
Can.	$4,000.00
U.S.	$3,000.00
U.K.	£1,900.00

Note: Prices refer to unpainted models, which are more valuable.

Photograph not available at press time.

See next image for shape outline.

Photograph not available at press time.

See previous image for Shape outline.

WARWICK HALL

Second Version
(Without name, 3 windows)

Code No.:	Unknown
Size:	5 ½", 14.0 cm
Backstamp:	B
Introduced:	1983-1983
Location:	Alderley Edge, Cheshire
Series:	English: Northern
Can.	$2,250.00
U.S.	$1,500.00
U.K.	£ 950.00

WARWICK HALL

Third Version
(Without name, 2 windows)

Code No.:	Unknown
Size:	5 ½", 14.0 cm
Backstamp:	C
Introduced:	1983-1985
Location:	Alderley Edge, Cheshire
Series:	English: Northern
Can.	$2,250.00
U.S.	$1,500.00
U.K.	£ 950.00

WASH DAY

Code No.:	866
Size:	2 ½", 6.4 cm
Backstamp:	O-2
Introduced:	1996-1997
Series:	Collectors Club
Can.	$50.00
U.S.	$35.00
U.K.	£20.00

WATER'S EDGE

Code No.: L2173
Size: 4", 10.1 cm
Backstamp: Q-2
Introduced: 1998 to the present
Series: English

Can. $240.00
U.S. $170.00
U.K. £ 59.95

WATERMEADOWS

Code No.: Unknown
Size: 3 ¾", 9.5 cm
Backstamp: M
Introduced: 1994-1994
Location: Osmaston, Derbyshire
Series: Anniversary Editions

Can. $225.00
U.S. $165.00
U.K. £110.00

WATERMILL
First Variation (Dark)

Code No.: Unknown
Size: 2 ¼", 5.7 cm
Backstamp: D
Introduced: 1985-1990
Location: Dorset
Series: English: South-West

Can. $70.00
U.S. $50.00
U.K. £30.00

WATERMILL
Second Variation (Light)

Code No.: Unknown
Size: 2 ¼", 5.7 cm
Backstamp: D
Introduced: 1990-1993
Location: Dorset
Series: English: South-West

Can. $70.00
U.S. $50.00
U.K. £30.00

WATERSIDE MILL

Code No.: 667
Size: 2 ½", 6.4 cm
Backstamp: M
Introduced: 1994-1999
Location: Shropshire
Series: English: Midlands

Can. $60.00
U.S. $45.00
U.K. £30.00

WATSON'S COLLECTIBLES

Code No.: L2267
Size: 3 ¼", 8.3 cm
Backstamp: R
Introduced: 1999 to the present
Series: American Landmarks

Can. N/A
U.S. $110.00
U.K. £ 45.95

WEALDEN HOUSE

Code No.:	Unknown
Size:	4 ½", 11.9 cm
Backstamp:	F
Introduced:	1987-1990
Location:	Sussex
Series:	English: South-East
Can.	$225.00
U.S.	$160.00
U.K.	£100.00

WEDDING BELLS

Code No.:	630
Size:	3 ¼", 8.3 cm
Backstamp:	K-1
Introduced:	1992-1999
Location:	Upleatham, Cleveland
Series:	English: Northern
Can.	$60.00
U.S.	$45.00
U.K.	£30.00

WELFORD GARLANDS

Code No.:	L2183
Size:	2", 5.0 cm
Backstamp:	Q-2
Introduced:	1998 to the present
Series:	Collectors Club
Can.	N/A
U.S.	N/A
U.K.	£9.95

WELLINGTON LODGE

Code No.:	432
Size:	2 ½", 6.4 cm
Backstamp:	J
Introduced:	1991-1995
Location:	Cheltenham
Series:	English: Midlands
Can.	$70.00
U.S.	$50.00
U.K.	£30.00

WENLOCK RISE

Code No.:	Unknown
Size:	6", 15.0 cm
Backstamp:	G
Introduced:	1988-1989
Series:	Collectors Club
Can.	$300.00
U.S.	$200.00
U.K.	£125.00

WESTMINSTER ABBEY

Code No.:	L2285
Size:	5 ¼", 13.3 cm
Backstamp:	R
Introduced:	2000-2000
Location:	London
Series:	Millennium
Can.	$550.00
U.S.	$475.00
U.K.	£150.00

"WET YOUR WHISTLE"™

Code No.: L2068
Size: 3 ½", 8.9 cm
Backstamp: O-2
Introduced: 1997-1999
Series: Coca-Cola™ Country

Can. $50.00
U.S. $35.00
U.K. £25.00

"WE'VE GOT IT....(OR THEY DON'T MAKE IT!)"™

Code No.: 894
Size: 3 ¼", 9.5 cm
Backstamp: O-2
Introduced: 1995-2000
Location: White Springs, Missouri
Series: Coca-Cola ™ Country

Can. $140.00
U.S. $100.00
U.K. £ 65.00

WHEYSIDE COTTAGE

Code No.: 613
Size: 2 ¾", 7.0 cm
Backstamp: K-1
Introduced: 1992-1998
Series: English: South-West

Can. $50.00
U.S. $35.00
U.K. £25.00

WIGHT COTTAGE

First Version (6.26 mm windows)

Code No.: 561A
Size: 2 ¾", 7.0 cm
Backstamp: H-1
Introduced: 1989-1990
Location: Isle of Wight
Series: English: South-East

Can. $90.00
U.S. $60.00
U.K. £40.00

WIGHT COTTAGE

Second Version (7.29 mm windows)

Code No.: 561B
Size: 2 ¾", 7.0 cm
Backstamp: H-1
Introduced: 1990-1994
Location: Isle of Wight
Series: English: South-East

Can. $90.00
U.S. $60.00
U.K. £40.00

WILLIAM SHAKESPEARE'S BIRTHPLACE

Style One, First Version
(With wording, dark green base)

Code No.: Unknown
Size: 3", 7.6 cm
Backstamp: A-1
Introduced: 1983-1983
Location: Stratford-upon-Avon
Series: English: Midlands

Can. $2,200.00
U.S. $1,500.00
U.K. £ 900.00

WILLIAM SHAKESPEARE'S BIRTHPLACE
Style One, Second Version
(Without wording, dark green base)

Code No.:	Unknown
Size:	3", 7.6 cm
Backstamp:	B
Introduced:	1983-1984
Location:	Stratford-upon-Avon
Series:	English: Midlands
Can.	$325.00
U.S.	$225.00
U.K.	£150.00

WILLIAM SHAKESPEARE'S BIRTHPLACE
Style One, Third Version
(Without wording, light green base)

Code No.:	Unknown
Size:	3", 7.6 cm
Backstamp:	C
Introduced:	1984-1989
Location:	Stratford-upon-Avon
Series:	English: Midlands
Can.	$140.00
U.S.	$100.00
U.K.	£ 65.00

WILLIAM SHAKESPEARE'S BIRTHPLACE 1989
Style Two, First Variation
(Grey windows)

Code No.:	Unknown
Size:	3", 7.6 cm
Backstamp:	H-1
Introduced:	1989-1989
Location:	Stratford-upon-Avon
Series:	English: Midlands
Can.	$350.00
U.S.	$250.00
U.K.	£175.00

WILLIAM SHAKESPEARE'S BIRTHPLACE 1989
Style Two, Second Variation
(Blue windows)

Code No.:	Unknown
Size:	3", 7.6 cm
Backstamp:	H-1
Introduced:	1989-1992
Location:	Stratford-upon-Avon
Series:	English: Midlands
Can.	$150.00
U.S.	$115.00
U.K.	£ 70.00

THE WINDMILL

Code No.:	L2224
Size:	5 ½", 14.0 cm
Backstamp:	R
Introduced:	1999 to the present
Series:	English
Can.	$110.00
U.S.	$ 70.00
U.K.	£ 28.50

WINDY RIDGE

Code No.:	L2007
Size:	3 ¾", 9.5 cm
Backstamp:	O-2
Introduced:	1996-1998
Location:	Middleham, North Yorkshire
Series:	English: Northern
Can.	$60.00
U.S.	$40.00
U.K.	£25.00

WINNIE'S PLACE

Code No.:	Unknown
Size:	6", 15.0 cm
Backstamp:	K-1, Limited edition
Introduced:	1992 in a limited edition of 2,000
Location:	Indiana
Series:	American Landmarks
Can.	$600.00
U.S.	$400.00
U.K.	£250.00

THE WINNOWS

Code No.:	Unknown
Size:	2 ½", 6.4 cm
Backstamp:	N-1
Introduced:	1996-1998
Location:	Castle Coombe, Wiltshire
Series:	Collectors Club
Can.	$90.00
U.S.	$60.00
U.K.	£40.00

WINTER AT HIGH GHYLL

Code No.:	Unknown
Size:	5", 12.7 cm
Backstamp:	K-1
Introduced:	1995 in a limited edition of 2,000
Varieties:	High Ghyll Farm
Location:	Lake District
Series:	English: Northern
Can.	$350.00
U.S.	$250.00
U.K.	£175.00

WINTER AT SKIRSGILL

Code No.:	L2208
Size:	3", 7.6 cm
Backstamp:	Q-2
Introduced:	1998-2000
Location:	Skirsgill
Series:	Visitor Centre Exclusive
Can.	N/A
U.S.	$50.00
U.K.	£19.95

WINTER'S WONDER

Code No.:	698
Size:	3 ½", 8.9 cm
Backstamp:	M
Introduced:	1994-1997
Varieties:	Autumn Hues, Spring Glory, Summer Impressions
Series:	A Year in an English Garden
Can.	$100.00
U.S.	$ 70.00
U.K.	£ 45.00

WISHING WELL

Code No.:	Unknown
Size:	2 ½", 6.4 cm
Backstamp:	None
Introduced:	1988-1989
Series:	Collectors Club
Can.	$160.00
U.S.	$115.00
U.K.	£ 70.00

WITH THANKS

Code No.:	L2276
Size:	3″, 7.6 cm
Backstamp:	R
Introduced:	1999 to the present
Series:	English
Can.	N/A
U.S.	$50.00
U.K.	£19.95

WITHAM DELPH

Code No.:	607
Size:	3 ½″, 8.9 cm
Backstamp:	J
Introduced:	1991-1994
Location:	Lincolnshire
Series:	English: Midlands
Can.	$140.00
U.S.	$100.00
U.K.	£ 65.00

WITLEY

Code No.:	L2204
Size:	4 ¼″, 10.8 cm
Backstamp:	R
Introduced:	1999-1999
Series:	Helen Allingham
Can.	$160.00
U.S.	$100.00
U.K.	£ 45.00

DE WOLHANDELAAR

Code No.:	120
Size:	5 ¼″, 13.3 cm
Backstamp:	J
Introduced:	1991-1998
Variations:	De Branderij
Series:	Netherlands
Can.	$65.00
U.S.	$45.00
U.K.	£30.00

Note: De Wolhandelaar's roof is grey, while De Branderij's is white.

WOODCUTTERS
First Version - 2 ½″

Code No.:	Unknown
Size:	2 ½ ″, 6.4 cm
Backstamp:	A-1, B
Introduced:	1983-1983
Location:	Devon
Series:	English: South-West
Can.	$350.00
U.S.	$250.00
U.K.	£175.00

WOODCUTTERS
Second Version - 2 ¼″

Code No.:	Unknown
Size:	2 ¼″, 5.7 cm
Backstamp:	B
Introduced:	1983-1987
Series:	English: South-West
Can.	$250.00
U.S.	$175.00
U.K.	£135.00

WOODMAN'S RETREAT

Code No.:	673
Size:	4", 10.5 cm
Backstamp:	M
Introduced:	1994-1995
Location:	Faringdon, Oxfordshire
Series:	Collectors Club
Can.	$175.00
U.S.	$125.00
U.K.	£ 80.00

THE WORLD FAMOUS OLD BLACKSMITH'S SHOP AT GRETNA GREEN

Code No.:	L2225
Size:	2 ¼", 5.7 cm
Backstamp:	R
Introduced:	1999 to the present
Location:	Gretna Green, Scotland
Series:	Britain's Heritage™
Can.	$160.00
U.S.	$100.00
U.K.	£ 39.95

WREN COTTAGE

Code No.:	Unknown
Size:	2 ¼", 5.7 cm
Backstamp:	J
Introduced:	1991-1993
Series:	Collectors Club
Can.	$200.00
U.S.	$135.00
U.K.	£ 85.00

WYCOMBE TOLL HOUSE

Code No.:	Unknown
Size:	2 ¾", 7.0 cm
Backstamp:	M
Introduced:	1994-1994
Series:	Special Editions
Can.	$400.00
U.S.	$275.00
U.K.	£175.00

YAIRD O' TARTAN

Code No.:	L2234
Size:	3", 7.6 cm
Backstamp:	R
Introduced:	1999 to the present
Series:	Scottish
Can.	$100.00
U.S.	$ 55.00
U.K.	£ 25.95

YEW TREE FARM

Code No.:	Unknown
Size:	3 ¼", 8.3 cm
Backstamp:	F
Introduced:	1987-1988
Location:	Cumbria
Series:	Collectors Club
Can.	$425.00
U.S.	$300.00
U.K.	£200.00

Note: Only 3,834 models were produced.

YORK GATE

Code No.: L2190
Size: 4 ¼″, 10.8 cm
Backstamp: Q-2
Introduced: 1998-2000
Series: Bed and Breakfast

Can. $130.00
U.S. $ 85.00
U.K. £ 35.95

YORKVALE COTTAGE

Code No.: L2042
Size: 3″, 7.6 cm
Backstamp: P-1
Introduced: 1997-1999
Location: North Yorkshire
Series: English

Can. $75.00
U.S. $45.00
U.K. £30.00

YULETIDE INN

Code No.: 414
Size: 5 ¼″, 13.3 cm
Backstamp: I-2
Introduced: 1990-1991
Location: Kent
Series: Christmas Specials

Can. $250.00
U.S. $175.00
U.K. £135.00

ZAANS KOOPMANSHUIS (DUTCH MERCHANT'S HOUSE)

Code No.: L2307
Size: 3 ½″, 8.9 cm
Backstamp: R
Introduced: 1999 to the present
Series: Dutch Heritage

Can. N/A
U.S. $50.00
U.K. £29.95

DE ZIJDEWEVER

Code No.: 121
Size: 6 ¼″, 15.9 cm
Backstamp: J
Introduced: 1991-1998
Varieties: Bloemenmarkt
Series: Netherlands

Can. $70.00
U.S. $50.00
U.K. £30.00

Note: The basement door on De Zijdewever is red, while Bloemenmarkt's is brown.

COLLECTING BY SERIES

A YEAR IN AN ENGLISH GARDEN
Autumn Hues
Spring Glory
Summer Impressions
Winter's Wonder

ALLEGIANCE COLLECTION
By Dawn's Early Light
Fourth of July
Home of the Brave
I Pledge Allegiance
I'll Be Home For Christmas
In Remembrance
One Nation Under God
Stars and Stripes Forever

AMERICA'S FAVOURITES
"Nothing Runs Like A Deere"
"See the USA in Your Chevrolet"
"Sign of Good Taste"
"This Bud's For You"
"Trust Your Car to the Star"

AMERICAN COLLECTION (1ST)
Adobe Church
Adobe Village
Cape Cod Cottage
Country Church
Covered Bridge
Forge Barn
General Store
Grist Mill
Lighthouse
Log Cabin
Midwest Barn
San Francisco House
Wallace Station

AMERICAN LANDMARKS
Afternoon Tea
Birdsong, The
Country Church
Countryside Barn
Covered Memories
Falls Mill
Fire House 1
Fresh Bread
Gold Miner's Claim
Great Point Light
Harvest Mill
Holy Night
Home For the Holidays
Home Sweet Home
Hometown Depot
Lobster at the Pier
Mail Pouch Barn
Nature's Bounty
Pepsi Cola Barn
Pioneer Barn
Rambling Rose
Riverside Chapel
Roadside Coolers
School Days
See Rock City
Seek and Find
Shave and a Haircut
Simply Amish
16.9 Cents per Gallon
Small Town Library
Spring Victorian
Victoriana
Watson's Collectables
Winnie's Place

AMERICA'S NATIONAL TREASURES
"Liberty Enlightening the World"
Old State House, 1776
President's House, The/ White House
Remember the Alamo
Shrine of Democracy/ (Mount Rushmore)

AN AMERICAN JOURNEY
Daydreams
Dog Days of Summer
Lace House
Morning Has Broken
Safe Harbour
Victorian Elegance

ANNIVERSARY EDITIONS
Cotman Cottage
Cruck End
Gertrude's Garden
Honeysuckle Cottage 1992
Pen Pals
Shades of Summer
Summer Days
Sweets and Treats
Watermeadows

BEATRIX POTTER™ COLLECTION
Buckle Yeat
Ginger and Pickles Shop
Hilltop
House of the Tailor of Gloucester, The
Tabitha Twitchet's Shop
Tower Bank Arms

BED AND BREAKFAST COLLECTION
Seaview
Tarnside
York Gate

BLAISE HAMLET COLLECTION
Circular Cottage
Dial Cottage
Diamond Cottage
Double Cottage
Jasmine Cottage
Oak Cottage
Rose Cottage
Sweet Briar Cottage
Vine Cottage

BRITAIN'S HERITAGE™ COLLECTION
Big Ben
Eros
Glamis Castle
Marble Arch
Micklegate Bar, York
Nelson's Column
Royal Albert Hall, The
Royal Pavilon Brighton, The
Shakespeare's Birthplace
Tower Bridge
Tower of London
World Famous Old Blacksmith's Shop at Gretna Green, The

BRITAIN'S HERITAGE COLLECTION™: ROYAL RESIDENCES
Balmoral
Buckingham Palace
Edinburgh Castle
Hampton Court Palace
Round Tower, Windsor Castle

CHRISTMAS ANNUAL ORNAMENT
Evergreens
Fir Tree Cottage
Great Expectations
Ivy House
Jingle Bells
Mistletoe Cottage
Plum Cottage
Robin Cottage
Santa's Corner
Silent Night

CHRISTMAS COLLECTION
Chestnut Cottage
Cranberry Cottage
Gingerbread Shop, The
Hollytree House
Partridge Cottage
Ring O'Bells
St. Joseph's Church
St. Joseph's School
St. Stephen's Church
Vicarage, The

CHRISTMAS IN AMERICA
Let Heaven and Nature Sing
To Grandmother's House We Go

CHRISTMAS LODGE COLLECTION
Eamont Lodge
Highland Lodge
Kerry Lodge
Snowdon Lodge

CHRISTMAS SPECIALS

Christmas Party
Deer Park Hall
First Noel, The
Frosty Morning
Old Vicarage at Christmas, The
St. Nicholas Church
Yuletide Inn

CLASSICS COLLECTION

Circular Cottage
Dial Cottage
Diamond Cottage
Double Cottage
Jasmine Cottage
Oak Cottage
Rose Cottage
Sweet Briar Cottage
Vine Cottage

COCA-COLA ™ COUNTRY COLLECTION

"A Cherry Coke-Just The Prescription"
Country Canvas
"Country Fresh Pickins"
Dixie Bottling Company
Fill 'Er Up and Check the Oil
Hazards of the Road
Hook, Line and Sinker
"Lunch Line, The"
"Milk For Mom and a Coke For Me"
"Mmm . . . Just Like Home"
Oh By Gosh, By Golly
Santa's Corner
Saturday Night Jive
"They Don't Make 'Em Like They Used To"
"Wet Your Whistle"
"We've Got It... (Or They Don't Make It!)"

COLLECTORS CLUB

Beekeeper's Cottage
Bridle Way
Cider Apple Cottage
Comfort Cottage
Cosy Corner
Crendon Manor
Curlew Cottage
Dovecot, The
Forget-Me-Not
Fresh Today
Gardener's Cottage
Good Life, The
Hampton Manor
Hampton Moat
Heaven Lea Cottage
Kiln Cottage
Lavender Cottage
Little Bee
Meadowsweet Cottage
Nursery Cottage
Petticoat Cottage
Porlock Down
Pottery, The
Puddlebrook
Pussy Willow
Spinney, The
Thimble Cottage
Wash Day
Welford Garlands
Wenlock Rise
Winnows, The
Wishing Well
Woodman's Retreat
Wren Cottage
Yew Tree Farm

DEALER SIGN

Bridge House Dealer Sign

DREAM COTTAGE MINIATURES COLLECTION

Bridge House
Chocolate House, The
Cotman Cottage
Honeysuckle Cottage
Old Mother Hubbard's
Paradise Lodge
Rose Cottage
St. Lawrence Church
Summer Haze
Titmouse Cottage
Toy Shop, The
Vine Cottage

DISNEYANA™ COLLECTION

Deck the Hall
Fire House 105
Hall of Presidents, The
Haunted Mansion, The
It's A Small World
Magic Kingdom Train Station / Magic Kingdom Memories
Main Street Cinema
Seven Dwarf's Cottage

DUTCH HERITAGE COLLECTION

Hollandse Poldermolen (Dutch Windmill)
Zaans Koopmanshuis (Dutch Merchant's House)

ENGLISH COLLECTION

Amazing Grace
Appleby East
Best Friends
Bill and Ben's
Birthday Cottage
Bobbins, The
Bobby Blue
Bottle of Cheer
Bowbeams
Buckle My Shoe
Bumble Bee Cottage
Burley Street Garage
Buttermilk Farm
Campden Cot
Canterbury Bells
Cat's Whiskers, The
Catkin Cottage
Chatsworth Blooms
Chatterbox Corner
Coach and Horses, The
Cockleshells
Country Living
Cowslip Cottage
Devon Leigh
First Snow at Bluebell
Flatford Lock
Free Range
George Inn, The
Golden Memories
Golden Years
Grandma and Grandpa's
Granny's Bonnet
Green Gables
Gulls Cry
Halcyon Days
Harebell Cottage
Harvest Home
Hermitage
Hideaway, The
High Spirits
Home is Where the Heart Is
Hubble-Bubble
I.N. Mongers & Sons
Kentish Brew
Lavender Lane
Lilac Lodge
Lion House, The
Little Water Mill
Lucky Charms
Make a Wish
Mangerton Mill
Medway Manor
Mosswood
Mother's Garden
New Neighbours
Nightingale
Old Crofty
Old Forge, The
Out For A Duck
Parson's Retreat
Pastures New
Pepper Mill Cottage
Playtime
Poppies, The
Puddle Duck
Right Note, The
Rock-A-Bye-Baby
Rose Bouquet
Sandcastle, The
Say It With Flowers
Scotney Castle Garden
Silver Bells
Smugglers' Rest
Stonemason, The
Sweet William
Temple Bar Folly
To Have and To Hold
Toadstool, The
Tuppenny Bun
Ullswater Boat House
Wagtails
Walker's Rest
Walton Lodge
Water's Edge
Windmill, The
With Thanks
Yorkvale Cottage

ENGLISH COLLECTION — MIDLANDS

Anne Hathaway's Cottage
Anne Hathaway's Cottage 1989
Armada House
Beehive Cottage
Birdlip Bottom
Bow Cottage
Bramble Cottage
Bredon House
Buttercup Cottage
Button Down
Chiltern Mill
Cobblers Cottage
Drapers
Elm Cottage
Farriers
Farthing Lodge
Fiddler's Folly
Fiveways
Four Seasons
Foxglove Fields
Granny Smiths
Izaak Walton's Cottage
Junk and Disorderly
Lace Lane
Ladybird Cottage
Lapworth Lock
Larkrise
Little Hay
Little Smithy
Magpie Cottage
Milestone Cottage
Moreton Manor
Paradise Lodge
Pear Tree House
Penny's Post
Railway Cottage
Riverview
Robins Gate
Rosemary Cottage
Rustic Root House
Saddler's Inn
St. Mark's Church
St. Mary's Church
Sulgrave Manor
Summer Haze
Tanners Cottage
Tillers Green
Tired Timbers
Titwillow Cottage
Tudor Court
Waterside Mill
Wellington Lodge
William Shakespeare's Birthplace
William Shakespeare's Birthplace 1989
Witham Delph

ENGLISH COLLECTION — NORTHERN

Beacon Heights
Bluebell Farm
Bridge House
Bridge House 1991
Bridge House in Winter
Brontë Parsonage
Burnside
Castle Street
Chatsworth View
Chocolate House, The
Dale Farm
Dale Head
Dale House
Dalesman, The
Derwent-le-Dale
Dove Cottage
Dovetails
Fry Days
Helmere Cottage
High Ghyll Farm
Holly Cottage
Holme Dyke
Inglewood
Keeper's Lodge
Lakeside House
Loxdale Cottage
Micklegate Antiques
Miners / Miners Cottage
Old School House
Potters Beck
Priest's House, The
Red Lion Inn
Runswick House
Rydal View
Sawrey Gill
Secret Garden
Ship Inn
Sore Paws
Spindles, The
St. John the Baptist
St. Lawrence Church
Stocklebeck Mill
Stoneybeck
Troutbeck Farm
Tuck Shop
Victoria Cottage
Village School
Warwick Hall
Wedding Bells
Windy Ridge
Winter at High Ghyll

ENGLISH COLLECTION — SOUTH-EAST

Acorn Cottage
Anchor, The
Anne of Cleves
April Cottage
Ash Nook
Bay View
Birchwood Cottage
Blue Boar
Boxwood Cottage
Brockbank
Calendar Cottage
Camomile Lawn
Chalk Down
Cherry Blossom Cottage
Cherry Cottage
Chine Cot
Clare Cottage
Cley-Next-The-Sea
Coach House
Coopers
Cradle Cottage
Crispin Cottage
Crown Inn
Daisy Cottage
Finchingfields
Flower Sellers
Flowerpots
Gables, The
Gossip Gate
Grantchester Meadows
Greensted Church
Honey Pot Cottage
Honeysuckle Cottage
Hopcroft Cottage
John Barleycorn Cottage
Kentish Oast House
King's Arms, The
Little Lupins
Marigold Meadow
Millers
Mrs Pinkerton's Post Office
Nutshell, The
Oak Lodge
Oakwood Smithy
Old Curiosity Shop, The
Old Shop at Bignor
Orchard Farm Cottage
Pargetter's Retreat
Primrose Hill
Rising Sun, The
Rustlings, The
Saffron House
Saxham St. Edmunds
Saxon Cottage
St. Peter's Cove
Stone Cottage
Strawberry Cottage
Sunnyside
Sussex Mill
Swan Inn
Swift Hollow
Tanglewood Lodge
Tea Caddy Cottage
Thatcher's Rest
Three Feathers
Toll House
Two Hoots
Wealden House
Wight Cottage

ENGLISH COLLECTION — SOUTH-WEST

Applejack Cottage
Briary, The
Butterwick
Cats Coombe Cottage
Chipping Coombe
Clover Cottage
Convent in the Woods
Creel Cottage
Cuddy, The
Dial Cottage
Double Cottage
Duckdown Cottage
Fisherman's Cottage
Fuchsia Cottage
Harriet's Cottage
Jasmine Cottage

ENGLISH COLLECTION — SOUTH-WEST (con't.)

Lazy Days
Moonlight Cove
Old Mill
Old Mine
Old Mother Hubbard's
Old Post Office, The
Ostlers Keep
Otter Reach
Out of the Storm
Periwinkle Cottage
Pipit Toll
Pixie House
Puffin Row
Purbeck Stores
Rose Cottage
Royal Oak Inn
Smallest Inns, The
Spring Bank
Spring Gate Cottage
Stradling Priory
Sweet Briar Cottage
Sweet Pea Cot
Tintagel
Titmouse Cottage
Vine Cottage
Watermill
Wheyside Cottage
Woodcutters

ENGLISH TEA ROOMS COLLECTION

Bargate Cottage Tea Room
Bo-Peep Tea Rooms
Grandma Batty's Tea Room
Kendal Tea House
New Forest Teas
Strawberry Teas
Swaledale Teas

FRENCH COLLECTION

L'Auberge D'Armorique
La Bergerie du Périgord
La Cabane du Gardian
La Chaumiére du Verger
Locmaria
Le Manoir de Champfleuri
Le Mas du Vigneron
La Maselle de Nadaillac
Le Petit Montmartre
La Porte Schoenenberg

GARDEN SERIES

Hestercombe Gardens
Leonora's Secret
Reflections of Jade
Tranquility

GERMAN COLLECTION

Alte Schmiede
Der Bücherwurm
Der Familienschrein
Das Gebirgskirchlein
Haus Im Rheinland
Jagdhütte
Die Kleine Bäckerei
Meersburger Weinstube
Moselhaus
Nürnberger Bürgerhaus
Das Rathaus
Rosengartenhaus
Schwarzwaldhaus
Strandvogthaus

HELEN ALLINGHAM

Chalfont St. Giles
Great Wishford
Midhurst
Witley

HISTORIC CASTLES OF BRITAIN

Bodiam
Castell Coch
Penkill Castle
Stokesay

IRISH COLLECTION

A Drop of the Irish
Ballykerne Croft
Donegal Cottage
Hegarty's Home
Kennedy Homestead
Kilmore Quay
Limerick House
Magilligan's
O'Lacey's Store
Pat Cohan's Bar
Quiet Cottage
St. Columba's School
St. Kevin's Church
St. Patrick's Church
Thoor Ballylee

LAKELAND CHRISTMAS COLLECTION

All Saints Watermillock
Borrowdale School
Langdale Cottage
Millbeck
Patterdale Cottage
Rydal Cottage

MILLENNIUM COLLECTION

Big Ben in Winter
Great Equatorial, The
Millennium Gate, The
Nelson's Column in Winter
Old Royal Obsevatory, The
Planetarium, The
Stargazer's Cottage
Westminster Abbey

MOMENTS IN TIME

"Bananas Are Back!"
"Our First Telly"
"Short Back and Sides?"
"Time Gentlemen Please!"

NETHERLANDS COLLECTION

Aan de Amstel
Begijnhof
Bloemenmarkt
De Branderij
De Diamantair
De Pepermolen
Rembrandt Van Rijn
Rozengracht
De Wolhandelaar
De Zijdewever

PAINT YOUR OWN

Ashleigh Down
Catmint Cottage
Essex Cottage
Flaxton Beck
Gypsy Cottage
Kentish Cottage
Little Birch
Marche House
Painswick Post Office
Reading Cottage
Roding Heath / High Roding
Rosy Rafters
Ruby Cottage
Shropshire Cottage
Suffolk Cottage
Suffolk Pinks
Warren, The

SCOTTISH COLLECTION

Amisfield Tower
Blair Atholl
Burns' Cottage, Alloway
Carrick House
Cawdor Castle
Claypotts Castle
Craigievar Castle
Crathie Church
Croft, The / Crofter's Cottage
Culloden Cottage
Culross House
Duart Castle
East Neuk
Edzell Summer-House
Eilean Donan Castle
Eriskay Croft
Fisherman's Bothy
Glenlochie Lodge
Hebridean Hame
Inverlochie Hame
John Knox House
Kenmore Cottage
Kinlochness
Kirkbrae Cottage
Lady Jane's Cottage
Ladybank Lodge
Loch Ness Lodge
Mair Haven
Pineapple House, The
Preston Mill
Salmon's Leap
Scotch Mist
7 St. Andrews Square
Stockwell Tenement
Yaird O' Tartan

SECRET GARDENS™ COLLECTION

Fragrant Haven
Fruits of Eden
Nature's Doorway
Peaceful Pastimes
Picnic Paradise
Tranquil Treasure

SPECIAL EDITIONS

Aberford Gate
Almonry, The
Amberley Rose
Arbury Lodge
Ashberry Cottage
Bermuda Cottage
Bridge House Dealer Sign
Bridge House in Winter
Butterfly Cottage
Candy Cottage
Chantry Chapel
Cliburn School
Clockmaker's Cottage
Cornflower Cottage
Counting House Corner
Dormouse Cottage
Finders Keepers
Gamekeeper's Cottage
Guildhall
Hadleigh Cottage
Leagrave Cottage
Mayflower House
Nest Egg
La Normadie
Oak Lodge
Olde York Toll
Ploughman's Cottage
La Provence
Queen Alexandra's Nest
Rainbow's End
Rose Cottage, Skirsgill
Rowan Lodge
Settler's Surprise
Star Inn, The
Syon Conservatory
Thornery, The
Vanbrugh Lodge
Victorian Romance
Wycombe Toll House

STREET SCENE COLLECTION

Street Scene No.1
Street Scene No.2
Street Scene No.3
Street Scene No.4
Street Scene No.5
Street Scene No.6
Street Scene No.7
Street Scene No.8
Street Scene No.9
Street Scene No.10

STUDLEY ROYAL COLLECTION

Banqueting House, The
Fountains Abbey
Octagon Tower
St. Mary's Church
Temple of Piety, The

VICTORIAN SHOPS COLLECTION

Apothecary
Book Shop
Haberdashery
Horologist
Jeweller
Pawnbroker
Tailor, The

VILLAGE SHOPS COLLECTION

Baker's Shop, The
China Shop, The
Greengrocer's, The
Jones the Butcher
Penny Sweets
Toy Shop, The

VISITOR CENTRE EXCLUSIVE

Aira Force
Dove Cottage - Grasmere
Honeysuckle Cottage III
Honeysuckle Trinket Box
Rose Cottage, Skirsgill
Winter at Skirsgill

WELSH COLLECTION

Brecon Bach
Bro Dawel
Bwthyn Bach Gwyn (Little White Cottage)
Castell Coch
Labour of Love
St. Govan's Chapel
Tudor Merchant
Ugly House

L2211 BIG BEN
Height: 22.0cm (8¾")
Since 1858, the chimes of Big Ben have rung out across London. Reputedly christened after the commissioner of works in charge of the rebuilding of the Houses of Parliament from 1834, Big Ben is actually the 13 ton hour bell inside the magnificent fretted stone clock tower, which reaches up almost 300ft.